ENVIRON...
CAREERS HANDBOOK

The Institution of
Environmental Sciences

TROTMAN

Second edition published in 1995 in Great Britain by Trotman and
Company Limited, 12 Hill Rise, Richmond, Surrey TW10 6UA

British Library Cataloguing-in-Publication Data
A catalogue record for this book is available from the
British Library

ISBN 0 85660 188 8

**The paper used for this publication has been
produced from sustainable plantations**

Typeset by Type Study, Scarborough
Printed and bound in Great Britain

LOGIC WILL GET YOU FROM A TO B

BUT WITH IMAGINATION YOU CAN CIRCLE THE WORLD.

ENGINEERING & SYSTEMS SPONSORSHIPS

Einstein was no fool, and when he said these words he meant it!

The principle he expressed then is equally valid now. And nowhere could this be more appropriate than at Ford today. With a pioneering history that brought motor transport within the reach of so many people, and a sales network that now circles the globe, it is impossible to overestimate the impact that Ford has had on the world.

Our continued success depends on many factors – not least of which is an intelligent, reasoned and logical approach to business. But it takes more than logic alone to make real progress and that is one of the reasons why we can offer such a unique and stimulating challenge to school leavers. In the motor industry, we are facing a time of greater change than ever before, and to meet these demands we rely on fresh ideas – from people with imagination.

Sponsorship is available to school leavers who plan to read either an engineering or a Systems/Information Technology degree at one of a number of approved higher education institutions. Students already at college should apply for our vacation training opportunities through their academic tutor.

For an information pack please write to Paul Mills, College Recruitment & Education Liaison, Room 1/360, Ford Motor Company Limited, Eagle Way, Brentwood, Essex CM13 3BW. Tel: 01277 252328.

These vacancies are open to both men and women regardless of ethnic origin in line with Ford's equal opportunities policy.

YOUR GRANT MAY BE FROZEN,

BUT OUR OVERDRAFT ISN'T.

Surviving on a grant alone may be worthy of some qualification.

That's why Midland offers an interest-free overdraft that rises from £500 for the first year, to £600 for the second and £700 for the third.

And, unlike some other overdraft facilities, it remains interest-free the whole time you're at college.

Free banking goes without saying, regardless of whether or not your account is in credit. On the odd occasion that it is, a handsome interest rate is paid on the balance.

The Autocheque card, with Switch facility, gives instant access to money 24 hours a day, 7 days a week, via the country's largest network of cash machines.

If you think you can handle credit, there's the option to apply for a fee-free Access and Visa card.

FOR FURTHER DETAILS CONTACT ANY MIDLAND BRANCH OR TELEPHONE 0345 180180

In the branch is the student advisor, who can both answer questions and explain further all the services available.

So, if you're interested in opening an account drop into your local branch, and see if Midland can help thaw you out.

MIDLAND
The Listening Bank

Member HSBC **◆X◆** *Group*

CONTENTS

ACKNOWLEDGEMENTS

Many members of the Institution and others have given freely of their time to prepare the first and second editions of the Environmental Careers Handbook. As well as those who prepared the first edition, I should like to thank the following for their help with the second edition: David Chambers and his students at Greenwich University, Derek Lohmann, the companies and individuals who provided information for the employer and career profiles and the colleges who responded to the course questionnaires.

John D. Baines
Chairman, Institution of Environmental Sciences

FOREWORD

I am very pleased that the Institution of Environmental Sciences has collaborated with the publishers Trotman to produce a second edition of the handbook on environmental careers.

There are increasing numbers of young people deciding that they wish to pursue careers which either help to improve or sustain the environment. There are others who, whilst not following a career which directly relates to the environment, are seeking to work for employers who have a 'green' ethic.

There are also increasing numbers of employers who are either involved in environmental protection or who are seeking to ensure that their business activities do not prejudice a sustainable environment.

It is no wonder therefore that many young people have great difficulty in becoming aware of the opportunities available to them. It is vitally important that we in the Institution help to utilise this enthusiasm especially during a period when jobs are hard to get.

The effort put into preparing the first edition was clearly worthwhile because it sold out in just over a year. The second edition follows the same structure but has been completely revised to include up-to-date information. The section on courses has been greatly expanded from just over 30 pages to 113 pages. This partly reflects the expansion in the number of environmental courses now available in colleges and universities.

I commend the handbook to those seeking an environmental career and to those who advise them. I wish all young people success in finding a career that will fulfil their ideals.

Duke of Westminster,
President of the Institution of Environmental Sciences

1   INTRODUCTION

BACKGROUND

The idea for the first edition of this handbook came from a workshop on 'Environmental Careers' held by the Institution of Environmental Sciences in September 1990. This was attended by members of careers advisory services in both the public and private sectors together with educational course leaders and employers. From the discussion it emerged that many felt they lacked sufficient information, for example, about career opportunities, what courses would be most suitable for any particular career, or where to look for information. It was reported that students and graduates who had an environmental 'vocation', or who wanted to work in a job connected with the environment found it very difficult to obtain guidance about suitable organisations – such as those with an environmental ethic who therefore might be an appropriate employer. It is against this background that the Environmental Careers handbook was born in 1993. The first edition proved so popular that it has been decided to publish an updated second edition. All the course material has been brought up to date and whole sections have been revised.

Career opportunities related to the environment have increased enormously in the last decade. In some areas these have overtaken the number of people looking for an environmentally-related career, let alone those qualified or experienced enough to tackle them. In other areas the opportunities are limited compared to the demand because of the high profile of the employer. One of the objectives of this handbook is to ensure that choices about career goals and courses are made in the light of better knowledge.

For many people, concern for the environment motivates their desire to engage in environmental work rather than a wish to use a relevant aptitude, qualification or experience. One of the aims of the Institution in producing this handbook is to help those who are keen to choose courses and a career which match their interests and capabilities, and then to achieve their personal goals. It is hoped that it will help employers also, by encouraging better self-selection among applicants, and in the long term, with courses more suited to their needs.

The handbook concentrates upon those careers normally approached via training at a university or college leading to a degree. Other careers are treated in less detail.

The treatment of the subject will focus on two main themes, namely: the career opportunities and the courses leading to the qualifications to enter those careers.

The information on courses is as comprehensive as practicable at the time of going to press. However, new courses are being set up and offered constantly. Equally, the number of potential employers is vast and details can be provided for only a selection. Whilst trying to provide a selection from all the main fields of interest, the sample from within each field has been arbitrary. The identification of organisations, which have a need to recruit perhaps as few as one environmental professional, is difficult. They do, however, exist, and we invite them to make themselves known to the Institution.

INTERDISCIPLINARY WORKING

Environmental issues often involve more than one subject area or career path, such as biology, chemistry or geography, for example.

Traditionally each subject area, both in terms of education and professional advancement, has developed within relatively narrow horizons. Each has its own technical vocabulary and its own career structure. These subject areas need to be brought together if there is to be a comprehensive understanding of environmental processes and issues. One of the main objectives of the Institution of Environmental Sciences is therefore to encourage interdisciplinary understanding and working.

More recently it has been increasingly accepted that there needs to be:

- cooperation and mutual understanding between the disciplines to enable there to be an effective use of resources

- integration of the results of their work in order that the environment is considered as a whole in making any decision based on that work.

Environmental specialists exist in great numbers, for example: acousticians, ecologists, wildlife specialists of many kinds, biochemists – it is possible to go on and list even more subdivisions of such fields of activity. Such specialists are essential. The Institution does suggest, however, that it is vital for the achievement of a sustainable future that all disciplines, especially the environmental ones, can understand and work with colleagues in other disciplines. A broadly-based education and experience enables professionals to ask the right questions of colleagues and others, and to evaluate critically the answers they receive.

It is therefore the policy of the Institution that any full professional Member must have had significant understanding and experience of interdisciplinary working. As will become obvious in various parts of this handbook, many employers are looking for traditional science or specialist training when recruiting inexperienced graduates. Advancement in almost all cases will, however, depend on the ability to understand and work with other disciplines. Throughout this handbook there will be an emphasis on this aspect of environmental careers and courses.

Senior posts, for example at management level, rely particularly on the ability to work in an interdisciplinary environment and the individual's original qualification becomes less important. However, when entering careers, those intending to become professionals will have to match their qualifications to those required by a prospective employer.

OUTLINE OF HANDBOOK

Chapter 2 provides a broad overview of the types of careers available. Chapter 3 expands upon this by providing details of typical employers, their work, the careers that they offer and the qualifications and experience required for entry into those careers. Some also discuss the in-service opportunities for training. These details of employers are complemented by profiles produced by some of the more recent entrants into environmental careers, covering such things as: how they got their jobs, what their day consists of, what skills are necessary, or whether the work is what they expected.

Chapter 4 provides advice on how to choose environmental courses. At this point it is necessary to distinguish between courses, and indeed careers, of a specialist and of a broader character. There are many careers that relate closely to the environment which involve a relatively narrow field of study such as acoustics/noise, epidemiology, meteorology, air pollution control, or water treatment. Others are more broadly based but still focused upon one field of activity and might include landscape or ecology. There are, however, other careers which require an interdisciplinary approach. Environmental assessment or auditing and environmental coordination in a manufacturing company, for example, require an understanding of many facets of the environment. These types of careers cannot be easily classified and do not have readily recognisable names. As a result the courses leading to such careers tend to have titles that are vague such as 'environmental sciences' or 'environmental studies'. Indeed entrants to such careers are often expected to be graduates in natural sciences: biology or other subjects are seen as providing a generally useful training background. This is why environmental courses and qualifications are sometimes seen as a second degree or supplementary qualification. Alternatively, a specialist course and career can be pursued to begin with; diversification into interdisciplinary working can take place later on in a career as the result of experience.

This handbook concentrates upon those courses of an interdisciplinary nature rather than the specialist ones. References to sources of information about the more specialised environmentally-related courses are, however, provided in the reference section.

Getting an 'environmental' job is in many ways no different from getting any other job except that in some cases there will be the need to demonstrate a vocational commitment. Applications have to be filled in, CVs provided and interviews negotiated. Where to look for job advertisements and directories of potential employers will be looked at in Chapter 5.

Trends which will affect career opportunities and the requirements for jobs in the light of such things as: the Single European Market, the need for languages, common and commercial skills – are discussed in Chapter 6.

Appendix I carries detailed information about the salary levels that can be expected in environmental careers. Appendix II contains detailed course listings of under- and postgraduate courses available, and a list of useful references.

THE INSTITUTION OF ENVIRONMENTAL SCIENCES

The Institution of Environmental Sciences itself is founded upon the belief that the interdisciplinary approach to environmental issues is vital. It also believes that there must be a professional career structure and a forum for discussion and exchange of information which embraces this interdisciplinary philosophy. The Institution exists and flourishes alongside and complementary to other more specialised institutions and indeed many of its members also belong to such institutions.

The Institution has recently reorganised and expanded its sequence of qualifications to reflect the need for professional development. It is now possible for new entrants to the profession to follow a planned progression leading to full professional Membership and ultimately Fellowship of the Institution. There is thus a close parallel with other professions, such as engineering, where employers provide a period of postgraduate training combined with appropriate experience leading to a recognised professional qualification. Members are welcome to join on the basis of a specialist qualification but those with an interdisciplinary qualification can progress more quickly through the grades of membership. The Institution requires that all members have experience of interdisciplinary working before achieving full professional Membership.

Further details can be obtained from:

The Honorary Secretary,
The Institution of Environmental Sciences,
14 Princes Gate, Hyde Park,
London SW7 1PU.

2   OUTLINE OF CAREER OPPORTUNITIES

The range of opportunities for those interested in an environmental career has mushroomed in the last decade and is now very great. This general outline and the individual employer profiles which follow in Chapter 3 illustrate the wide range of careers that now exist.

This chapter is divided into three sections which indicate:

- opportunities of a broadly interdisciplinary environmental nature
- the types of organisation which provide career opportunities
- the size of the career market.

TYPES OF ACTIVITY

By its nature one of the major interests of an environmental career is that you will almost certainly be working within an interdisciplinary framework. At any stage of a career you will be expected to assist colleagues and clients and liaise with others in other branches of environmental work and in other disciplines altogether, for example in engineering or accountancy.

The work itself is a continuous learning process and you may be involved in developing and using computer skills one day, writing reports or getting boots muddy whilst doing field studies the next. The hours of work are often irregular and, as with other professions, time scales are often short. However, with enthusiasm, dedication and a good team spirit the satisfaction can be great.

The following section looks at those mainly interdisciplinary activities which might form part of an environmental career. Most types of organisation offering an environmental career encompass a range of these activities; at the end of this section there is a table indicating where you are likely to have the opportunity of engaging in your preferred activities.

Consultancy

A consultant's role is usually purely advisory but occasionally a client will delegate executive authority to manage an activity, such as surveys or control of certain construction works. Where more integration is required with the client's management team, individual consultants may be brought in and work under the client's overall direction. Consultants' services are used because the client, who could even be in another part of the same organisation:

- does not have the required expertise
- has insufficient personnel
- requires a second opinion, for example, by an independent audit.

Examples of work might include:

- developing environmental management systems
- undertaking environmental audits
- verifying company environmental statements
- carrying out environmental impact assessments
- advising on how to minimise the environmental impact of a development

or many of the other jobs described in this section.

Design/planning

Design or planning may relate to any of a range of activities trying to establish behaviour or future function. Examples might include:

- designing instrumentation to monitor air pollution
- the engineering design of a process plant to keep within pollution emission limits, or to assure the quality of a water supply
- the strategic planning of a company management structure and systems to ensure that a company has a green image and obtains registration under BS 7750 (see Environmental auditing, below).

A whole new area of planning has opened up following the UN Conference on Environment and Development in 1992. The Government committed itself at the conference to finding ways to achieve sustainable development, in other words development that does not diminish the capacity of the environment to support life and livelihoods. At government level initiatives have been set up to bring environmentalists, developers, industry and government together to plan a sustainable future. At local level, several towns have already set up Local Agenda 21s which bring local government and communities together to find ways of achieving sustainability at community level. At both national and local levels there are likely to be increasing employment opportunities in helping set up and maintain such processes.

Education/training

Most initial environmental education and training is done at educational establishments by college lecturers with specialialist knowledge of the environment. Such lecturers may run or contribute to specialist courses such as ecology; interdisciplinary courses such as environmental sciences; or may bring an environmental awareness into the education of other disciplines such as engineering. Increasingly, new entrants to such a career will need a teaching qualification in addition to their technical one.

Training can take place during working hours for specific projects or jobs. Further opportunities for more general career enhancement may be provided in various ways:

- on-the-job by direct experience and by guidance from more experienced colleagues
- by gaining a spread of experience under the guidance of a senior member of the employer's staff, as is required by some professional institutions
- short commercial courses and conferences
- in-house training courses
- distance learning: for example, through the Open University.

Providers of such training can therefore be found within the employer's organisation, commercial training companies or educational establishments.

Environmental auditing

As with financial auditing, environmental auditing means establishing what is going on and checking that certain standards of performance are met by companies or organisations. Environmental auditing may look at a range of issues: a local authority's activities; a factory's compliance with environmental regulations/planning consent conditions; the manner in which a consultancy or a food retailer is behaving; or the level of contamination in land or buildings when they are bought or sold.

The British Standard on Environmental Management Systems (BS 7750) requires that companies manage their affairs in a way that is responsive to environmental issues. It does not lay down environmental standards but recommends that:

- standards are set
- the company has a systematic management approach to achieving and continually improving them
- staff know of the standards
- the company's affairs are audited against those standards.

The standard is complementary to BS 5750 on Quality Assurance. As a general rule, a company that is well managed environmentally is well managed generally, and is an efficient organisation.

The European Commission's Eco-Labelling scheme relates to the 'cradle to grave' effects of products and requires a 'life cycle' assessment. Producers have to be audited before a label can be awarded.

Environmental planning

Planning with environment in mind has the overall objective of achieving sustainable development. It takes into account the inter-actions between the types of land use, their demands for transport, their use of energy as well and emissions of greenhouse gases, as well as other direct and indirect effects on the environment. Within this broad framework much of the work is concerned with ensuring that individual land uses or activities are compatible with the protection of the environment, so that Sites of Special Scientific Interest (SSSIs), the landscape, or the amenities of existing and future developments, for example, are not adversely affected. Environmental planning may be planning to re-create a habitat or to maintain a habitat effectively in the face of pressures that might destroy it. A major related objective is often socio-economic development, in other words, the creation of jobs, the provision of local education, health services and leisure activities.

Environmental Impact Assessment

Environmental Impact Assessment (EIA) or Environmental Assessment (EA) is the prediction of the consequences, both good and bad, of a particular proposed development or development strategy across all aspects of the environment, often including the socio-economic aspects. It is applied by law to major development projects such as motorways, factories, reservoirs or mines. It usually involves significant consultation with those who are likely to be affected and with those responsible for natural resources such as ground water, surface water, air quality, noise, disposal of waste, and traffic. EIAs of projects are often subject to considerable review by, for example, a local planning authority, by people who object to the plans, in difficult cases by the Government, and in exceptional cases by the European Commission. They are often therefore the subject of controversy at public inquiries relating to a planning application. Environmental scientists are very likely to be required to give evidence at such inquiries on behalf of the interested parties, such as the developer or objecting residents. The environmental appraisal of plans and policies is very similar to the assessment of projects but is less well developed and practised.

A 'Life Cycle Assessment', sometimes described as 'cradle to grave', is an assessment of the environmental impacts of, say, a product or building from the raw material stage, through processing/ manufacture/building, distribution and selling, to its use and re-cycling or disposal as waste. Such assessments would cover such things as the use of energy, water and non-sustainable resources.

Environmental management

Environmental management is usually practised to achieve environmental goals. It could involve the management of:

- an area of land to preserve or create a habitat and landscape, such as a heathland of special scientific interest which requires the equivalent of grazing or regular burning to maintain a prized set of characteristics

- a factory to minimise waste and meet pollution emission control conditions

- the manufacture, distribution and use of products in an environmentally aware manner and on a 'cradle to grave/life-cycle' basis to permit the award of an EU 'Eco-Label'

- a company which believes it has an environmental conscience

- a company which from self-interest wishes to minimise resource

use and waste creation, maximise recycling and ensure environmentally safe disposal

- the supply of water and the disposal of sewage.

Mediation/consensus-building

Mediation is well established in North America and is becoming
increasingly popular in Britain where in relation to the environment it
is generally known as consensus-building. In the process, mediators
or facilitators bring the various interested parties together to seek a
solution acceptable to all of them while remaining neutral themselves. They are sometimes supported by technical teams, also
neutral, who can provide information about the suitability and
impact of the solutions being considered.

Consensus-building is increasingly being recognised by the environmental movement as a better alternative to the adversarial
approach of finding solutions to environment and development
problems. It is being used by government to try and involve as many
interests as possible in the development of the UK Sustainable
Development Strategy and by local authorities to encourage sustainability among local communities under the banner of Local Agenda
21. Opportunities for careers in this area are likely to increase
substantially over the next few years.

Rangers

Rangers, wardens or conservation officers are employed to look after
areas of land and wildlife, such as parks or nature reserves, to help
maintain them, ensure their survival, educate the public and
encourage and assist people to enjoy them without harming the
source of their enjoyment.

Regulation

Many regulatory authorities such as Her Majesty's Inspectorate of
Pollution (HMIP), the National Rivers Authority (NRA), the River

Purification Boards in Scotland, the Water Service in Northern Ireland, the Ministry of Agriculture, Fisheries and Food (MAFF) and local planning and environmental health authorities have a dual role. On the one hand they set environmental, emission and effluent standards and on the other they monitor and enforce compliance with the standards. They liaise with public and private businesses and if necessary take legal action. These responsibilities will change when the new Environment Agency is created in 1995. It is expected that the Agency will combine the responsibilities of HM Inspectorate of Pollution, the National Rivers Authority and Waste Regulatory Authorities.

Research

Environmental research may be one of two types. Applied research and development helps to indicate how to solve problems, control adverse effects and maximise benefits; ways of achieving certain aims may be developed, such as pollution control or waste neutralisation. Research may be short-term to solve specific, usually local, problems or medium to long-term to solve global problems. Broadly, pure or fundamental research is aimed at increasing our knowledge and understanding of the systems involved, for example, ecosystems, or the propagation of noise and its effects. One example of such research is the international Climatic Change programme analysing the physical, chemical and biological processes which make up the carbon-cycle to determine the impact of the increase in the concentration of the 'greenhouse' gases in the atmosphere. The ultimate aim is to develop a strategy to control those environmental effects regarded as adverse.

Environmental impact assessments may entail some initial research in the sense that facts have to be established about the existing environment which were not known beforehand, such as discovering the existence of rare species of fauna. Certain environmental effects may need to be investigated and the results added to the store of knowledge and understanding. In industry, a process engineer may need to research and develop a novel way of treating waste products so that they may be recycled rather than discharged.

Surveying, measurement and monitoring

Surveys and measurements are carried out for a variety of reasons, for example:

- to establish baseline data – these are standard measurements taken to provide a starting point for the assessment of changes and trends, for example in air or water quality
- to find out what is there, such as species of flora and fauna in a field
- to establish levels of pollution which:
    - exist before a development takes place
    - are created during its construction or demolition
    - are created during its life
    to compare with any limits set or predictions made.

Most measurements are done in-house by an industrial company or a regulatory authority, but sophisticated work may call for the services of a specialist service company. In the past, measurements have been largely of a 'one-off' nature. There is now an increasing demand for continuous monitoring of discharges and this in turn is leading to an increasing demand for specialists in instrumentation.

In this example particularly, and indeed in many others, it is not only graduates or those with Higher National Diplomas who are required for the work. The traditional divide between those who are professionally qualified and 'technicians' is breaking down. There is an increasing realisation that a 'technician' is part of the team. Recognition is increasing for supporting technical staff who perhaps do the majority of field work, or who look after and use very expensive analytical equipment. Indeed, they are often more difficult to recruit because the good ones are in short supply. It is, however, an area of employment which is underdeveloped; in fact, because of the shortage, graduates and even postgraduates are often used for such tasks for which they may be totally unsuited. It is encouraging that some colleges are now setting out to train technicians to provide these vital services.

Related professions

In many businesses today environmental concerns are being linked to health and safety at work because many of the changes introduced to protect people also help protect the environment. In local authorities environmental health which covers food and hygiene also covers noise, dust, air pollution and drinking water quality.

TYPES OF EMPLOYER

Many of the environmental activities mentioned above can be found within a variety of types of employers. The types of organisations which can provide a career for the environmentally aware and competent person include:

Specialist environmental consultancies Work in this area may be as part of a large team (in the hundreds), in a small more tightly-knit one (less than ten), or as a self-employed individual providing services both to clients directly and indirectly as a sub-contractor to other consultancy organisations. The work involved may be specialised, as in noise, water ecology or applied psychology; somewhat broader, such as measurement, analysis and prediction of a range of pollutants; or very broad, for example, environmental impact assessment or the management of such interdisciplinary studies.

Engineering/planning consultancies and other professional companies Many engineering and planning consultancies provide environmental consultancy services within the framework of their wider services (with staff numbers in hundreds and thousands). The same is increasingly true of accountants, management consultants, finance houses, solicitors and surveyors. In many ways the technical work is similar to that in the specialised consultancies but a vital difference is the considerable liaison necessary with colleagues in non-environmental disciplines and the greater degree of interdisciplinary working. The opportunities to branch out from purely environmental work and to influence the wider thinking and policy are correspondingly increased.

Business and Industry A broad spectrum of industrial organisations, such as manufacturing industry, mining companies as well as developers of property, new manufacturing installations, roads, railways, and so on may have in-house teams to look after their environmental obligations and interests. Virtually all industry has some concern in this respect. Many will employ a consultant as and when the need arises. Most will have someone who, nominally at least, has responsibility for the environment over matters like discharge or effluent, disposal of waste, relationships with neighbours, or the health of the workforce. The bigger organisations and those with an obvious potential impact on the environment, such as the utilities providing gas, water, electricity and oil, waste disposal operators and chemical manufacturers, will employ staff to coordinate and oversee their environmental duties. These staff may be managers, advisers, auditors, control engineers, monitoring or process scientists. The very large companies, such as the utilities and multi-nationals, will employ significant numbers of specialist environmental staff as well as using consultants to cope with problems on an *ad hoc* basis, or specialist needs beyond the competence of their staff, or perhaps to provide a credible independent view.

Equipment and plant suppliers Industrial and other organisations use a large amount of instrumentation to monitor the environment and their discharges into it. They also need the means of controlling the impact upon the environment, perhaps to reduce dust emissions, to clean water before discharging, or to neutralise waste. Such hardware has to be developed, designed, manufactured, tested, sold and serviced. Hardware manufacturers need to know and understand the performance required from their equipment in terms of measuring or controlling pollution. This is likely to need the advice of an environmental professional.

Regulatory agencies These exist to ensure that laws and regulations are complied with. In England and Wales, all regulation is likely to be undertaken by the Environment Agency due to be created in 1995. In Scotland and Northern Ireland the regulatory authorities will remain. The following are for Scotland: HM Industrial Pollution Inspectorate, River Purification Boards and regional, islands and district councils. In Northern Ireland the Environment Service, Planning Service and the Water Service are responsible for regulation. Jobs in these organisations involve helping to frame standards or legislation, knowing the relevant legislation, and being able to monitor what is happening 'on-site'. They also involve an understanding of the wider context because very often what should be done involves a judgement of what is reasonable to expect by way of improvement in a particular situation, discussing ways of solving the problem and ultimately, if all else fails, taking enforcement action.

Research and development organisations No practical work is possible without a prior understanding of environmental systems and of the ways in which they can be protected and managed. This means that there has to be considerable research into, and monitoring of, the environment. This is often done by universities and colleges of higher and further education. However, much is carried out at establishments funded by particular sectors of industry, commercial organisations and by government, such as the Natural Environment Research Council, English Nature, the Countryside Council for Wales, Scottish Natural Heritage, and the Department of the Environment.

Education and training institutions Little, if any, environmental work could happen without the appropriate training and education of personnel. Very often the training of others is combined with consultancy, research and development. Education in training is not restricted to the universities or colleges. It can be provided by professional bodies, commercial organisations offering services to industry or in-house within an industry itself, in relation to specific aspects of the work. These organisations will often use staff from colleges, consultants or practitioners from industry as tutors.

Non-governmental organisations (NGOs) There are hundreds of NGOs all pursuing their own interests and the interests of their members. Some, like Friends of the Earth and Greenpeace mainly lobby to bring about changes that favour the environment. Others, like the Royal Society for the Protection of Birds focus on a particular aspect of the environment and work for its protection. Organisations such as the British Trust for Conservation Volunteers provide opportunities for people to get involved as volunteers in environmental improvement projects. Some of these receive some financial support from the government, others rely on donations and subscriptions. Many rely heavily upon voluntary help but all have some professional staff. In this sector especially it is possible to have an environmentally supportive career without being an environmental professional. Campaigns need to be run to raise awareness and educate people about issues, or raise funds and recruit volunteers. These activities need to be managed and regional networks organised. In addition there is the need for conservation and environmental science professionals in these organisations.

Environmental management organisations Many bodies have a direct role in managing the environment, such as the Countryside Commissions, the National Parks Authorities, and the Forestry Commission. These and others who hold large areas of land, such as the National Trust, the water companies and local authorities employ ecologists, rangers, conservation and countryside officers.

Financial organisations Increasingly banks, insurance companies and investment fund managers are looking at the environmental implications of their loans and investments, and the larger firms of accountants are providing environmental audit services to their clients (see also Engineering/planning consultancies, above). Some institutions now specialise in ethical investments. Investments are only made in companies that meet their stringent environmental and other criteria.

International bodies There are a few international environmental organisations providing employment opportunities although positions are hard to obtain. The United Nations environmental and education agencies are funded by national governments and operate like government organisations. The most important international NGOs covering environment are the **World Conservation Union** (formerly the International Union for Conservation of Nature and Natural Resources or IUCN for short), the **Worldwide Fund for Nature International** and the **International Institute for Environment and Development**. All have opportunities for environmental careers especially for those with multilingual abilities.

Consultants and freelance staff can work for any of the types of organisation described above by providing skills and experience not available in-house or by helping out during peak periods of activity. The opportunity exists for self-employed experts to get together by creating networks of like-minded people to assemble teams for particular studies or tasks. Some take the form of agencies, rather like secretarial agencies, identifying and introducing staff to work in a client's premises or for the client on a temporary basis. It is by working for a variety of clients in this manner that an environmental career can be pursued progressively and expanded.

   Within organisations career progression may be easier but may be limited in technical scope by the interests of the organisation. In industry, careers are likely to develop more in a managerial sense than in a technical sense. It is nonetheless important that the higher levels of management in industry have an awareness and understanding of environmental issues and take responsibility for them.

   Even within organisations having no obvious commitment to the environment and no clear role for interdisciplinary environmental professionals, there may well be the opportunities for an 'environmental' career to develop. Professional chemists, managers and engineers with an interest in environmental issues have often been able to take on an increasing range of environmentally-related responsibilities, for example:

- works managers or engineers, via water or waste management, could become responsible for environmental policy

- physicists, via meteorology, could research the environmental effects of climate change due to increased levels of greenhouse gases

- acousticians, via minimising noise, might be involved in planning improvements in neighbourhood amenity and health

- landscape architects, via planting designed to improve the appearance of developments, may have a wider involvement in the ecosystem and the conservation of flora and fauna

- agricultural economists, via food policies, could become involved in environmental management of the countryside

- marine scientists, via fish population studies, might progress to the conservation of endangered species.

These examples indicate the overlap between the responsibilities of many professions and the more obviously environmental ones. The Institution of Environmental Sciences believes that environmental awareness and education ought to be an essential part of the background policy or commitment of any educational or training establishment and should be integrated into the training of all professionals. It is neither just something for a few specialists, nor something which should be treated as an optional extra for others.

Having previously identified the types of activity that may be of interest to you, table 1 is an attempt to indicate the organisations in which they are most likely to be found. Some examples of each type of employer can probably be found encompassing any particular activity. The table can only attempt to indicate broad generalities.

Table 1. Employers and their likely activities

Employers \ Activities	Environmental planning	Design/planning	Assessment/appraisal	Auditing	Management	Regulation	Rangers/wardens	Research	Training/education	Measurement/monitoring	Surveying	Consultancy	Mediation
Environmental Consultancies	X	X	X	X	X			X	X	X	X	X	X
Engineering/Planning	X	X	X	X	X			X		X	X	X	
Business/Industry	X	X	X	X	X			X	X		X	X	
Equipment/Plant suppliers		X						X	X	X			
Regulatory Agencies			X	X		X			X				
R & D organisations		X						X		X	X	X	
Education establishments	X	X						X	X	X	X	X	X
Non-Governmental Organisations				X	X		X	X	X	X	X	X	
Conservation Bodies	X	X		X	X		X	X	X		X	X	
Financial Organisations			X	X									
International Organisations	X		X	X		X		X	X				
Waste Contractors	X	X	X	X	X					X			
Water Companies	X	X	X	X	X			X		X	X	X	
Laboratories					X			X		X		X	

THE SIZE OF THE ENVIRONMENTAL JOB MARKET

Opportunities in the various sectors of employment will vary considerably. Some of the more obvious ones, such as consultancy and regulatory agencies, may receive many unsolicited applications from graduates and others without much experience when what they really want is staff with experience. This is often a 'Catch 22' situation with the employers wanting the experience but people not being able to obtain it unless they have employment. This means that to gain some experience in the first place you may need to work as a research assistant or technician providing support to more experienced people. Alternatively, experience can be gained by working as a volunteer for one of the environmental non-government organisations. For example, many of the wardens of RSPB reserves began by working as volunteers during their holidays. 'Budding' environmental professionals can also begin by pursuing a more specialised environmental career making use of a specialist qualification, or post-graduate research, or pursue a related career, such as town planning or engineering and gradually switch to concentrating on environmental matters.

The main thing at the start of a career is to get into an organisation which deals with or should deal with environmental topics or issues even if the initial job appears to be somewhat peripheral to your long-term career goals. It may help to have some idea of the size of the various sectors of the job market, however. No attempt has been made in this guide to produce a rigorous or a highly accurate survey, merely to draw together various data and estimates that have been made by others and to fill some of the gaps with approximate guess-work. In many cases the total number of staff given will include administrative support and other professionals whose work is not necessarily of an environmental nature. Some of the data which follows has come from directories which would also be of help in finding a suitable employer. A list of such directories is to be found at the end of the book (see references).

Numbers of jobs

The last 25 years has seen more than a ten-fold increase in the number of UK organisations offering environmental consultancy services. There are now about 350, as well as a much smaller number based elsewhere in Europe. The UK consultancies themselves are taking a considerable interest in Europe, especially in the former eastern bloc countries where they have nearly 30 branches. The 'environmental component' of such organisations ranges in size from one to about 150 professionals. This implies a total of the order of 5,000. In addition there is a significant number, in the hundreds, of self-employed professionals in this sector.

There is a wide range of environmental management and conservation bodies and non-governmental organisations (NGOs), of varying sizes. Some are fully professional, such as the Countryside Commission with 320 staff, English Nature with approximately 700 staff, the Countryside Council for Wales with 300 staff and Scottish Natural Heritage with about 720 staff. Others rely more on volunteers but still have a core staff, for example, the National Trust has 3,000, taking some 40 school leavers a year. The Groundwork Foundation has 42 local Groundwork Trusts and between them they employ nearly 600 professional/technical staff and about 107,000 volunteers. The British Trust for Conservation Volunteers has around 180 staff in its two main offices, 90 field staff and approximately 62,000 volunteers. Conservation Volunteers Northern Ireland has about 25 permanent staff as well as volunteers. The Woodland Trust has approximately 140 permanent staff, the Centre for Alternative Technology has 30, and the Wildlife Trusts (Royal Society for Nature Conservation) has about 500 people working in its 47 wildlife trusts and 50 urban wildlife groups. The eleven national park authorities each have between 30 and 350 staff. Other bodies are English Heritage and the countryside, leisure/recreation sections of local authorities who, for example, employ rangers to look after country parks.

Non-governmental organisations are often inundated with applications and may be more interested in volunteers than recruiting paid staff. Opportunities for professionals are limited. Organisations include the Royal Society for the Protection of Birds, Friends of the Earth, Greenpeace and local pressure groups. The World Wide Fund For Nature (WWF) in the UK has about 180 staff. In the directories produced by the Civic Trust and The Environment Council over 1000 organisations (NGOs, professional institutes and so on) are listed as being involved in or interested in the environment even though some simply have only a 'watching' brief.

Banks, investment trusts, insurance companies, accountants, management consultants (some describe part of their activities as 'environmental consultancy' – see types of employers, page 16) often employ environmental professionals of whom some are full-time but others are part-time consultants. At least 50 management consultants claim to provide environmental services.

Industry presents a totally different pattern of employment. Some companies may have sizeable environmental teams, but the majority have only one or two environmental professionals. They will be involved in developing policies and objectives, but responsibility for implementing environmental improvements is delegated to line managers. These are drawn from a variety of disciplines and will continue to be so. Environmental coordinators, recycling and policy managers should have a more inter-disciplinary background. The total number of significant industrial organisations in the UK is around 50,000. The top 5,000 business enterprises each employ more than 400 people and have a sales turnover of more than one million pounds. If it is assumed that each has an average of one or two professionals with some responsibility for the environment but who may be not trained environmental professionals this gives a *potential* employment market of 5,000 to 10,000.

Regulatory organisations can be very large and employ many who would not be regarded as environmental professionals as such. The National Rivers Authority has about 6,500 staff and Her Majesty's Inspectorate of Pollution about 300. Local authorities (in environmental health, planning and waste) probably have 5,000 to 10,000 environmental professionals and the Department of the Environment 500.

Research is likely to be mainly based within universities or in what traditionally has been the public/government sector although there is increasingly a commercial/applied emphasis. The Natural Environment Research Council is an umbrella organisation for government research stations with a total staff of 2,500. Individual stations include the Institute of Terrestrial Ecology (250), the British Geological Survey (800), the British Antarctic Survey (400), and the Institute of Oceanographic Sciences (160). Other centres are the Water Research Centre (500), ICI's Brixham Environmental Laboratory

(120), the Warren Spring Laboratory of the Government's Department of Trade and Industry (300) and the Building Research Establishment (300).

With the advent of 'Green Consumerism' and more recently of 'Eco-Labels', suppliers of consumer products and domestic equipment need increasing support from consultants and staff to audit suppliers and supplies from 'cradle to grave'.

There are 10 to 15 large wholesale food suppliers including the bigger farming companies and importers and a number of the large retailers who have become aware of the need to present an environmentally friendly image for their products. They are building up groups to vet their own and their suppliers' products. There are probably about 50 environmental professionals currently involved and the number is likely to grow substantially.

There are over 100 universities and affiliated colleges of higher education (including the former polytechnics), plus hundreds of other colleges in the UK. In Appendix II there are numerous interdisciplinary courses listed and for each one of these there are probably about ten more of a specialised nature, such as noise or landscape. There are about 150 degree courses with the words 'environment' or 'environmental' in the title although some are specialist courses with an environmental module tacked on. The education sector therefore employs about 5,000 professionals to teach on such courses alone, added to which are those who provide HNC, HND, postgraduate and professional on-the-job or part-time training. What should not be forgotten either is the very important role of the many thousands of school teachers who are needed to sow the seeds of an appreciation of and a concern for the environment among schoolchildren in many different subject areas. The Field Studies Council has ten centres each with between two and four tutors and some also have research assistants and conservation officers. Not all those wanting an environmental career can achieve full-time employment relating directly to the environment, but their input can nonetheless be crucial to its longer-term protection.

Overall nearly three quarters of a million people (mainly in crafts and manual work) have been estimated as employed in the UK directly or indirectly on environmental conservation, although more than half of these are in the building industry. Of the rest 12,000 are in full-time landscaping and wildlife conservation plus 130,000 active volunteers and 6,500 in archaeology. Most of these jobs will require vocational rather than academic qualifications.

Over 100,000 people are employed in pollution control, recycling and waste management industries. Alongside this, 26,000 environmental management jobs exist in polluting industries and 14,000 in regulatory agencies (these last two figures are not necessarily additional to those referred to previously). In the polluting industries about five to ten per cent of the figures or 1,500 represent professional 'scientific' jobs. Suppliers of equipment and instrumentation are said to employ nearly two-thirds of those concerned with achieving satisfactory control of air and water quality and the management of waste and land remediation, i.e. removal or neutralization of contamination, for example by dangerous chemicals from industrial developments. This represents a total of about 70,000 although presumably a large number will be concerned with the manufacture of standard items, for example for sewage works and so on, rather than doing purely environmental work.

International bodies have a high profile and are relatively numerous. They include the United Nations Environment Programme based in Kenya but with offices throughout the world, the World Conservation Union (formerly the International Union for the Conservation of Nature and Natural Resources) based in Switzerland, the World Wide Fund For Nature (International) also based in Switzerland and the European Commission in Brussels. The total staffing of these is in the thousands. However, it should be borne in mind that the staffing is international and so the UK share, which in some cases is set by protocol, is limited and often drawn from the civil service.

These figures are very approximate but they do give an indication of the scope for employment in the environmental field. Many of those holding such jobs will have 'grown into' them and others will continue to follow them. Whilst many jobs are now offered to environmental specialists, many others will continue to be filled by those who have not only developed their own skills whilst on the job but have developed the job itself.

WHAT QUALIFICATIONS ARE NEEDED?

This is a hard question to answer because both environmental careers and employers cover such diverse interests. There are vocational courses appropriate to certain environmental careers such as town and country planning, landscape management, environmental management and environmental health and if you are interested in one of these careers it is advisable to write to the relevant professional association for further advice. Where there are no obvious courses linked to a particular career in the environment, the most sensible approach is probably to take a first qualification in a traditional subject in an area of personal interest such as geography, engineering, natural science or environmental science and follow this up with a second qualification which provides an added environmental dimension to your expertise.

The following tables give some idea of the opportunities but they are no more than an indication. They refer to a first degree only; clearly a combination of first and second degrees widens the options available and the chances of getting a job. Table 2 indicates the degree subject which by itself is most likely to provide the means of entering a particular profession. Table 3 suggests which professions might offer a graduate with a degree already the best or most appropriate opportunity of a job, other things being equal, such as disregarding an excess of graduates with similar degrees.

A degree is only a means of getting a foot in the door which opens on to an environmental profession. Anyone who wishes to follow this profession must be prepared for a lot of hard work in a variety of areas. No area of activity is barred to those with clear ambitions who are prepared to persist, learn, work hard, and if necessary do any work at all related to the environment to build up gradually the experience and understanding necessary to 'qualify' for their chosen profession. This may sound daunting but such a career can be materially rewarding, very enjoyable and often leads to great job satisfaction.

Table 2. Degree courses in the environment

The table below summarises the first degree course you should be taking for your particular interest in the environment:

Interest	Archaeology	Agriculture	Architecture	Biology	Chemistry	Engineering	Environmental Health	Environmental Sciences	Estate Management	Geography	Geology	Law	Land/Landscape	Mathematics	Physics	Surveying	Town and Country Planning	Toxicology
Atmospheric Pollution	–	L	M	H	M	L	H	–	L	–	L	M	–	M	–	–	H	M
Consultancy	L	M	M	H	H	H	H	M	M	M	M	H	M	M	L	M	H	M
Education	–	M	M	M	M	M	M	L	M	M	L	M	L	M	L	L	M	L
Field studies	M	L	H	L	–	L	L	M	H	H	–	L	M	L	H	H	L	L
Industry	–	L	L	H	H	M	L	L	–	–	L	M	L	L	–	–	M	M
Inspection	–	–	M	H	H	H	H	L	L	M	L	H	M	L	–	L	M	L
Instrumentation	–	–	–	M	H	L	M	–	L	L	–	H	M	–	–	–	L	L
Liquid Effluent/Sewage	–	–	M	M	H	L	M	–	L	M	–	M	L	L	M	–	M	M
Monitoring	–	–	M	M	M	H	H	–	L	L	–	M	M	L	L	L	H	M
Planning	–	H	L	–	M	L	M	H	M	M	M	–	H	H	L	H	L	–
Regulations	–	M	M	M	L	M	M	M	L	M	M	L	M	M	–	L	M	L
Research	L	M	H	H	H	H	M	L	M	M	L	H	L	L	L	L	H	M
Safety	–	L	M	H	H	H	M	L	L	L	L	M	M	L	L	–	M	M
Solid Waste	–	–	L	H	H	M	M	L	L	M	L	L	L	M	L	–	L	M
Water	–	–	M	M	H	M	M	L	M	M	L	L	L	L	M	L	H	M

Relevance of degree to interest

H High M Medium L Low – Unlikely to be any

Table 3. Career opportunities in the environment

The table below summarises the areas where you can best put your first degree to use in the environment

Type of Work

Degree	Industry	Inspection/Regulations	Planning	Research	Equipment/Instrumentation	Field Centres	Education	Safety	Monitoring/Analysis	Water	Liquid Effluent/Sewage	Solid Waste	Atmospheric Pollution	Consultancy
Archaeology	–	L	M	M	–	H	L	–	–	–	–	–	–	M
Agriculture	–	–	L	M	–	H	L	L	–	L	M	L	–	L
Architecture	L	L	H	L	L	–	L	–	–	–	–	–	L	M
Biology	L	L	L	M	L	H	M	L	M	M	L	M	M	M
Botany	L	L	L	M	L	H	M	L	M	M	L	M	M	M
Zoology	L	L	L	M	L	H	M	L	M	M	L	L	M	M
Ecology	L	L	M	M	L	H	M	L	M	M	M	M	L	M
Chemistry	H	H	L	M	M	L	M	M	M	M	H	M	M	H
Engineering — Chemical	H	M	L	M	M	L	M	H	M	M	H	H	M	H
Civil	L	L	H	L	M	–	L	M	L	H	H	M	L	H
Electrical/Electronics	M	L	L	L	H	–	L	M	L	L	L	L	L	M
Environmental Health	L	M	L	L	M	M	M	H	H	M	M	M	M	M
Environmental Sciences	L	M	M	M	M	M	H	M	H	M	M	M	M	H
Estate Management	L	L	H	L	–	M	L	L	L	L	L	L	M	M
Geography	L	L	H	M	L	H	M	L	L	H	M	M	L	H
Geology	L	M	M	M	L	H	M	L	L	H	H	H	L	H
Law	L	H	M	–	–	–	L	M	–	M	M	M	M	M
Land/Landscape	L	M	H	–	–	M	L	L	–	L	L	–	L	M
Mathematics Modelling	L	M	M	H	L	–	M	M	M	H	H	L	H	H
Physics — Acoustics	H	H	H	L	M	–	L	H	H	–	–	–	M	H
Meteorology	–	–	L	H	M	L	L	L	H	M	L	–	H	L
General	M	L	L	M	M	L	M	M	M	M	M	M	M	L
Surveying	H	M	H	L	L	L	L	M	L	M	L	M	M	L
Town and Country Planning	L	M	H	L	–	L	L	L	L	L	L	L	M	M
Toxicology	M	L	–	H	L	L	M	H	H	H	H	H	L	H

Relative level of interest likely to be shown by employer
H Most likely interest M Medium interest L Low interest – Unlikely to be any interest

3 EMPLOYER AND CAREER PROFILES

The previous chapter is a broad overview of the types of careers available. This chapter expands upon this overview by providing descriptions of typical employers, their work, the careers that they offer, the qualifications and experience required for entry into those careers and the means by which they recruit staff.

The details of employers are complemented by information produced by some of their more recent entrants into environmental careers. These profiles cover such things as, how they got their jobs, what their day consists of, what skills are necessary and whether the work is what they expected.

You will find frequent mentions of the 'university milk round'. This is an arrangement whereby organisations visit universities during pre-arranged periods to meet and interview interested potential graduates. Good 'prospects' will often be invited to the organisations offices for further discussions.

In order to help locate details and profiles that may be of interest to you, they are arranged in broadly the order used in the previous chapter for the discussion of types of employer. They are listed below:

Consultancy and Environmental Engineering
Environmental Resources Management; Ove Arup & Partners; Wimpey Environmental.

Industrial – Waste Management
Greenways Landfill.

Industrial – Manufacture
IBM.

Industrial – Chemical
Dow Chemical Company Limited

Industrial – Utilities
British Gas PLC; National Power.

Regulatory Agencies
The National Rivers Authority; Belfast City Council.

Research and Monitoring
Laboratory of the Government Chemist; The Natural Environmental Research Council; Silsoe Research Institute.

Non-Governmental Organisations
Greenpeace; The Royal Society for the Protection of Birds; WWF UK (World Wide Fund For Nature).

Retail/Distributive Companies
Body Shop.

Corporate
British Airways PLC

Education and Training
Teaching (Manchester Metropolitan University)

CONSULTANCY AND ENVIRONMENTAL ENGINEERING

ENVIRONMENTAL RESOURCES MANAGEMENT 8 Cavendish Square, London W1M 0ER

Founded in 1971, ERM claim to be Europe's leading environmental consulting firm with extensive experience in environmental management. They have over 250 clients from more than 80 countries around the world; many are leading names in industries such as oil and gas, chemicals, transport, manufacturing electronics, textiles, construction and even financial services.

Number of employees: 250 professional staff.

Typical staff: Project leaders, consultants.

Number of staff taken on: Varies from 10 to 20 annually, divided equally between newly qualified and job changers, and consultants.

Qualifications: Primarily post-graduates. Exceptional graduates considered particularly with relevant work experience. Degree in environmental/natural sciences, engineering, social science or business field.

Recruitment methods: No problem finding people unless moving into a new area. Occasionally advertise in the *New Scientist, Economist*, or *ENDS* (environmental magazine.) Recruits often head-hunted by former colleagues now in ERM. Worth writing a speculative application.

Work placements: Occasionally for students working on MSc project.

Key business areas include strategic consulting, environmental auditing, waste management, environmental assessment, site investigation, policy and planning, and energy and economics. The work is very diverse and demanding.

Typical recent projects include developing a comprehensive central hazardous waste treatment facility in South East Asia for the Hong Kong Government; assisting British Rail in the planning of the Channel Tunnel rail link; studies of the EU on policies to address acid rain and the greenhouse effect, and management of the UK ODA's portfolio of environmental projects in Chile.

Projects vary in length from under a month to over two years and the size of teams ranges from two people to over 70 professional staff. Excellent opportunities exist to undertake projects and secondments abroad.

Consultancy work is not for everyone. It is extremely demanding in terms of time, commitment and energy. You need to be a self-starter with an analytical approach to problem solving, be able to carry considerable responsibility and be able to appreciate and balance both the commercial and the environmental needs. It is not an easy, but is certainly a rewarding career.

Profile

Joanne Cochrane, 34, BSc in Environmental Sciences, University of East Anglia, MSc in Environmental Technology (Energy Policy), Imperial College, London. Has been with ERM for nine years.

'In early 1986 I joined ERM's Hong Kong office which at that time was a very small operation (it now has a staff of over 50). During my two and a half years in Hong Kong I focused mainly on management of Environmental Impact Assessments (EIAs), risk and noise assessments, before returning to the UK in 1988 to do an MSc.

In 1989, I returned to ERM and am now a Technical Director in ERM's International and Policy Services Division. As such, I am responsible for the operational management of all our work for the international development banks and donors (such as the World Bank, UNDP, UNIFO, ODA, EBRD, ADB). Current projects that I am directing include an air pollution control strategy in China, a portfolio of environmental projects in Chile, and EIA training in Jordan. The wide range of challenging projects in exotic (though not always easy) locations is a large part of what motivates most of the international team. During my five years in the international division, I have carried out numerous projects in countries ranging from North Korea, to Lithuania, Cyprus, Yemen, Gabon, and Chile to mention just a few.

OVE ARUP & PARTNERS 13 Fitzroy Street, London W1P 6BQ

Arup Environmental is a specialist group within Ove Arup & Partners and has a wide range of technical expertise in environmental and related disciplines, including environmental assessments and audits, regional and urban planning studies, mineral resource development, derelict and contaminated land redevelopment, solid waste disposal, environmental legislation and policy, landscape design, water resources development, noise and vibration and economics.

There are some 40 professional staff engaged totally in environmental issues with another 60 people (such as acoustics, noise and vibration consultants) whose work has a strong environmental element. The diversity of skills means Arup Environmental can undertake a wide range of projects throughout the world, working in conjunction with engineering colleagues in other parts of the firm.

Typical recent projects include: environmental assessment for new motorway and widening schemes; strategic environmental and economic studies and detailed air quality assessments for the Channel Tunnel Rail Link project; development of nature conservation strategy for Peterborough Southern Township; and developing the reclammation strategy for the Pride Park site, Derby, for which we are currently supervising its implementation.

Number of employees involved in environmental issues: 100

Typical staff: Environmental scientists, environmental planners, environmental engineers, landscape architects. Also specialists in areas such as acoustics, archaeology, chemistry, computing, ecology, economics, geotechnics, hazard and risk assessment, hydrogeology, land use planning, materials technology, soil science.

Qualifications: Graduates usually with a PhD or MSc. Also experienced consultants. Occasionally technicians with HND.

Likely number of vacancies: 5–6 annually of which 2–3 are graduates.

Recruitment method: Specialist press, the university 'milk-round' and recruitment agencies. Many people write in with speculative applications.

Occasional work experience and industrial placements opportunities.

Profile

Joanne Bole, 24, joined Arup Environmental in 1992 with a degree in Geography from University College London. After six months she was given a leave of absence to take an MSc in Environmental Engineering at Newcastle University and returned to Ove Arup a year later.

'I joined Ove Arup six months before starting my MSc and worked on a variety of projects including environmental assessments as part of environmental statements for the M4 Relief Road, Redhill Aerodrome and M1 widening. I also spent six months working as a member of a multidisciplinary team for design and route definition of the country section of the Channel Tunnel Rail Link Project. Although my input on most of these projects was a supporting and administrative one, I learned a great deal about the type of work involved in various aspects of environmental consultancy

Since my return to Ove Arup, on completion of my MSc, I have worked on a number of air quality assessments as part of environmental statements for both new motorway and motorway widening schemes. I have also assisted in the preparation of reports and rebuttals for public inquiry with respect to contaminated land and air quality.'

WIMPEY ENVIRONMENTAL Beaconsfield Road, Hayes, Middx UB4 OLS

It was the rise in public concern about environmental issues and the resulting increase in legislation during the late 1980s that led the

George Wimpey Group to set up Wimpey Environmental in 1990. Since then the consultancy has developed rapidly and undertakes over 600 contracts a year.

Wimpey Environmental provides a comprehensive and independent environmental consultancy service to commercial, industrial and public sector clients. Their main areas of understanding are in the physical, chemical and biological environment: contaminated and derelict land; environmental risks in the workplace; energy, water quality and asbestos in the built environment; environmental pollution from noise and atmospheric emissions from industrial sites; surveys and assessments in the marine environment.

These consultancy and project management services are supplemented by a strong capability in data collection, laboratory analysis and baseline survey reporting.

It is an experienced and highly streamlined organisation with offices in Hayes, Swindon, Cardiff, Plymouth and Warrington. Overseas work is undertaken with prime interests in South East Asia and Europe.

Typical projects: environmental assessments of power stations, oil terminals and chemical process plants; water quality risk assessments in buildings; contaminated land audits and rehabilitation schemes; oceanographic engineering investigations.

Number of employees: 190

Typical staff: Consultants, graduates and post-graduates, technicians.

Qualifications: Environmental sciences, geology, hydrology, hydrogeology, geotechnics engineering, environmental science and chemistry, acoustics, noise and vibration, chemical analysts, geochemistry, soil science, oceanography, biology, marine biology, marine chemistry, physical oceanography (or any water type degree). Software/computer sciences, particularly with geographical information system experience. Technicians–analytical and electronic skills with HNC, HND, BTEC.

Number of vacancies: Approximately 30 annually: 6 technicians, 8 graduates, 8 postgraduates, 6 or 7 consultants.

Recruitment method: Technical press – *New Scientist, ENDS, World Water, Acoustics Bulletin*. Local press for technicians.

Training: Career development. Professional skills such as negotiating, report writing and marketing awareness. Day-release to study for higher qualifications for some scientists and technicians.

Profile

Rachel Martyn, 27, graduated in Economics and Agricultural Economics at Exeter University. She travelled for a year and gained work experience in a variety of temporary employment before taking an MSc in Rural Resources and Environmental Policy at Wye College, London University, sponsored by Wimpey. She joined Wimpey Environmental eighteen months ago.

'I am a member of the small but growing Environmental Assessment, Management and Auditing team. (Environmental Assessment is a legislated process which assesses and predicts the environmental impacts of a **proposed** *development, while Environmental Auditing is the tool for verifying whether an* **existing** *organisation is meeting environmental regulations, or even operating to higher standards.)*

My job is essentially a mixture of marketing and project management. In a competitive market, there is always a need to find future work while carrying out existing projects. This ranges from cold calling potential clients and following up with a letter or meeting, to writing proposal documents following invitations to tender. My involvement with existing projects has largely been as project co-ordinator for multi-disciplinary project teams, pulling together expertise from sub-consultants and from all over the organisation, such as soil specialists, ecologists, hydrogeologists, noise and vibration scientists, landscape planners, highway and transport specialists etc. I also provide written input to reports as required and assist in the overall editing of draft and final reports.

Coordination of a multi-disciplinary project also comprises a substantial amount of administration to ensure that all team members are aware of new developments, changes to the original terms of reference, meetings etc. The coordinator's main responsibility is to maintain client contact and to keep tabs on project costs so that they do not run over budget.

The advantage of working in a multi-faceted organisation such as Wimpey Environmental is that there are always new skills to be learned and areas to understand. I occasionally assist our specialists on site investigations and this provides an opportunity to learn how to use specialist equipment and conduct different forms of site survey.

It was soon after graduating that I first realised my interests lay in environmental consultancy work, but my first degree was not directly relevant and I had to take a further degree. I wrote to 40 consultancies, having selected their names from an environmental directory, to seek financial support. Many were prepared to consider me for employment after I had graduated, but Wimpey were also in a position to offer me sponsorship.'

INDUSTRIAL – WASTE MANAGEMENT

GREENWAYS WASTE MANAGEMENT The Ridge, Chipping Sodbury, Bristol BS17 6AY

Greenways is a national waste management company responsible for safe disposal of waste in controlled landfill sites. The company also operates its own waste transport fleet and household recycling centres.

To ensure they meet their environmental responsibilities Greenways retains specialist advisers to assess all new developments for environment impact; installs systems to control noise, dust, litter, pests, water pollution and landfill gas; sets up community care programmes involving local people for individual sites; rigorously monitors operational and closed sites; and has a programme of site restoration.

Greenways regards waste as a resource which can be utilised for the creation of energy and recycling back to the production stream. The company was the first to export electricity generated from landfill gas extraction projects to the National Grid and has the capacity to generate 14 MW of electricity.

It is a young, dynamic company, most of its management staff (Unit and Operations Managers) are graduates under 30 years of age.

Number of employees: 160

Typical staff: Drivers, plant operators, unit managers, Operations managers, technical managers for monitoring and analytical work, technicans.

Qualifications: Managers: geologists, possibly with chemistry, environmental chemists, engineering/geology, soil scientists.

Likely vacancies: Up to four annually.

INDUSTRIAL – MANUFACTURE

IBM PO Box 41 North Harbour, Portsmouth PO6 3AU

IBM woke up early to the need for environmental action. As the world's foremost manufacturer of computer systems and subsystems, and Britain's fifth largest exporter, they have been a committed leader in environmental issues for over 20 years and were one of the first companies to lay down a formal environmental policy. This has been supported over the years by a US $1 billion investment in capital equipment for environmental protection.

Recent environmental initiatives include the following:

- The development of engineering techniques to recover and recycle the materials used in the manufacture of hardware, so today up to 90 per cent of the materials now used in IBM computers could be recovered.

- From being one of the largest CFC users (mainly as cleaning solvents) in the mid-1980s, IBM have a target for the elimination of CFCs and methyl chloroform from products well ahead of EU regulations. IBM UK phased out CFCs from all of its operations at the end of 1992, and methyl chloroform from the end of 1993.

- Recently undertaken steps to ascertain shareholders views on the significance of IBM's environmental impact, which will serve as an agenda for the future.

- The existence of an Environmental Affairs Group to manage and coordinate the company's business practices in the UK and assess their impact on the environment. Now all IBM locations throughout the UK, including the PC manufacturing site and software laboratory, have environmental performance targets to reach.

- The setting up of a war on waste programme aimed at all employees, giving them an opportunity to air their views and concerns. To raise their awareness of environmental initiatives through a quarterly newsletter, and to highlight areas where improvements could be made.

- Cooperation with Portsmouth University to establish an MSc course in Environmental Engineering.

Computer systems are an invaluable tool for environmental scientists and planners in assembling data, analysing trends and exploring alternative courses of action. IBM provide the equipment, the software and the technical support for such projects.

Qualifications: All degree disciplines with a special emphasis on engineering sciences, maths/statistics, computing

Recruitment methods: The university 'milk-round' when jobs are available.

Number of staff taken on: Currently not recruiting.

Work placements: Occasionally.

Profile

Kieran Mayers, 21, an Environmental Science student at Bradford University, started his year's industrial placement in the summer of 1994 at IBM's manufacturing site at Havant.

'I was instantly impressed by the environmental standards adopted by the company; environmental issues were high on the business agenda.

I was immediately given an active role, and within three weeks was involved in the management of the recycling facilities, designing colour presentations, organising an exhibition week and representing the company at various forums, to name but a few of my responsibilities.

The support from my colleagues was also good. They allowed me to develop my own ideas, and no suggestion I made was ever ridiculed, despite my inexperience.

IBM offered me every opportunity to get 'hands on' experience of Environmental Management and Health & Safety issues within industry.'

INDUSTRIAL – CHEMICAL

DOW CHEMICAL COMPANY LIMITED Lakeside House, Stockley Park, Uxbridge, Middx UB11 1BE

The fifth largest chemical company in the world, Dow manufactures and markets chemicals, plastics and performance products, hydro-carbons and energy, and consumer specialities – which include agricultural products and consumer products.

In the UK Dow has two manufacturing sites at Barry, in Wales, and the largest at Kings Lynn, which occupies a site of 75 acres, and employs nearly 200 staff.

Dow is committed to reducing by 50 per cent all emissions of priority substances by 1995. Key to Dow's environmental policy is a network of some 250 professionals including industrial hygienists, toxicologists, epidemiologists, physicians and other health and environmental scientists throughout the world. A large number of chemists and chemical engineers also work on environmental issues, seeking to improve products and manufacturing processes.

Typical environmental positions in the UK: Environmental engineer: new post for engineer with some eight years' experience to oversee environmental issues at all sites.

Chemical engineers who join as graduate trainees and, having gained wide experience within Dow, undertake environmental projects. Current number – 24 including three new graduates and 6 with under three years' experience. Recruitment through targeted universities – Bath, Bradford, Leeds, Surrey, Birmingham.

Occupational health, safety and environmental professionals – who have gained membership of the relevant institute. Currently two on site.

Chemists with experience of the chemical industry brought in to work on specialist environmental projects.

INDUSTRIAL – UTILITIES

BRITISH GAS PLC Heron House, 326 High Holborn, London WC1 7PT

British Gas is growing and developing worldwide. As well as supplying gas to 18 million domestic and business customers in Great

> **Typical staff:** Graduates and postgraduates in environmental sciences, chemistry with an environmental bias, biochemists, geochemists, microbiologists, occasionally geologists.
>
> **Likely vacancies:** Graduate opportunities could occur for most of the above.
>
> **Recruitment method:** Graduate recruitment workshops and vacancies are notified through careers services.

Britain, it has developed an international business in the exploration and production of oil and gas, and is exporting its wealth of expertise to new and developing markets.

Natural gas is the cleanest of the fossil fuels. It produces less carbon dioxide than coal and oil, and no dust, smoke or ash. It is also a highly efficient energy source.

However, environmentally, British Gas are not complacent. Initiatives have included – £100 million spent seeking ways to save energy; assisting in the reduction of heavy pollution in central Europe through the introduction of natural gas; helping Athens with air pollution to ancient monuments; a strong Research and Development programme to support reclamation of contaminated land; and the introduction of environmental audits at every site in their business. Finally, look carefully at the next British Gas van you see; is it powered by natural gas?

British Gas has a Corporate Safety and Environment department but each business, eg Transco, Exploration and Production, is responsible for implementing the Company's environmental policy in its own operations. Construction has an environmental planning unit largely concerned with environmental aspects of new construction. This involves dealing with consultants, local communities, planning authorities, the National Rivers Authority and local environmental pressure groups. Typical staff employed are ecologists, landscape engineers, geographers and town planners.

The Research and Technology department at British Gas also plays a major role in the company's environmental activities and supplies environmental skills to other areas of British Gas such as exploration and production. At British Gas, environmental considerations are part of every project team whether it is laying a new pipeline, reclaiming a site, or building an installation. The Research and Technology function has a staff of about 1000.

NATIONAL POWER Windmill Hill Business Park, Whitehill Way, Swindon, Wiltshire, SN5 6PB

National Power is the UK's leading electricity producer. While many of its power stations burn coal for fuel, other energy sources are oil, water or windpower. Gas is being used increasingly in a new generation of power stations.

Over the past five years the company has spent £1.7 billion on environmental improvement initiatives. These include Britain's first and world's largest flue gas desulphurisation plant at Drax power station. To reduce nitrogen oxide emissions, its largest coal stations are being filled with special burners. National Power is also investing in commercial windfarms, gas exploration and acquisition, and Combined Heat and Power projects. Several operating sites have established environmental study centres and nature reserves.

All new projects undergo environmental assessments. Environmental audits now monitor the company's progress towards continuous environmental improvement. Standards of care and concern for the natural world are also applied to its growing portfolio of overseas power developments.

The company aims to integrate its environmental policy into all business units. Environmentalists are employed in many areas of the company including research and planning. A small corporate environment unit is responsible for environmental policy development and environmental auditing. All staff are trained in the environmental implications of their job and British Standard BS7750 is being widely adopted for environmental management at major operating sites. Drax power station has been a pilot site for the European Union's Eco-Management and Auditing Scheme.

Typical staff: Largely scientists and engineers including: chemists, ecologists, biologists and chemical, mechanical, electrical and electronic engineers.

Recruitment method: National and specialist press.

Training: Largely on-the-job, augmented by general management courses. Support to take technical and professional qualifications.

Jobs in the water industry

Job areas of major environmental impact to be found in the water industry:

Conservation: scientists responsible for the environmental impact of any new development, habitat creation, landscaping, heritage, and the implementation of environmental policy.

Sludge Application: scientists look at the environmental effect of putting sludge back on the land.

Environmental Impact: monitors the effect of fully treated sludge when recycled into the river system.

Marine Science: monitors the quality of bathing water around the coast and looks at big engineering schemes pumping effluent into the sea.

Water Resourcing: looks for new sources of water, where to put bore holes and so on.

Research and Development: seeks better ways to treat sewage.

Trade Effluent: polices the substances that industry discharge into the sewers, negotiating effluent contracts.

REGULATORY AGENCIES

THE NATIONAL RIVERS AUTHORITY River House, Waterside Drive, Aztec West, Almondsbury, Bristol BS12 4UD

'Guardians of the water environment' is how the NRA describes its role. It is the strongest Environmental Protection Agency in Europe

---

Typical staff: The NRA takes on graduates and A level school leavers to work in: pollution control – making sure water quality is protected; water resources – ensuring water reserves are at an environmentally satisfactory level; flood defences – building barriers against the sea to protect property and wildlife habitats; fisheries – inspectors and water bailiffs to protect and monitor fish stocks; recreation – keeping the balance between conservation and leisure pursuits; conservation – working to preserve and enhance the landscape and wildlife; navigation – regulating navigation on our rivers. Many departments offer scientific analytical work.

Qualifications: Graduates – first degree, MSc and PhD in environmental sciences, chemistry, biology, geography (scientific), hydrology, analytical chemistry, ecology, marine biology. Occasional openings for solicitors and in information technology, finance and personnel. School-leavers with GCSEs and A levels with a scientific bias.

Recruitment methods: All year recruitment. Specialist/technical press – *Civil Engineering, New Scientist*. Also national press – watch *The Guardian* and *Independent*.

with wide-ranging powers. Formed in 1989 when the ten water authorities were privatised, its many responsibilities include managing and developing water resources, pollution control, flood defence, fisheries protection, conservation and navigation. Over the next four years it expects to spend £2 billion on these core activities.

The NRA operates through ten regions based in river catchment areas throughout England and Wales and has a staff of around 7,500.

From 1 April 1996 the NRA will merge with Her Majesty's Inspectorate of Pollution and Waste Regulators to form the **Environmental Agency**.

BELFAST CITY COUNCIL Health and Environmental Services Department, Belfast City Hall, Donegal Square, Belfast BT1 5GS

Belfast City Council's Health & Environmental Services Department provides four main services: Building Control, Environmental Protection, Health Protection and Promotion and Consumer Protection. Environmental Health Officers are employed in the three latter services.

Environmental Protection: This includes the monitoring and control of a wide range of environmental pollutants including air, noise, water, radiation and contaminated land. A strong emphasis is placed on proactive work by assessing the environmental impact of new developments.

Health Protection and Promotion: EHOs are responsible for enforcing the Health and Safety at Work Act 1974 in commercial and recreational premises. This involves inspections, investigation of accidents and the provision of advice on how to protect employees and members of the public using the premises. EHOs inspect the condition of privately rented dwellings including houses in multiple occupation and investigate complaints of harassment of tenants. Other duties include the management of Pest and Dog Control Services. Information and advice as well as structured training courses are also provided.

Number of employees: There are approximately 300 Environmental Health Officers in Northern Ireland, 63 of whom are employed by Belfast City Council. There are also two Scientific Officers, ten Technical Assistants and a Business Support Team.

Qualifications: To become a qualified EHO you need to be accepted on an approved course at a University or College. The Chartered Institute of Environmental Health Officers (CIEH, Chadwick Court, 15 Hatfields, London SE1 5DJ) can provide a list of establishments offering approved courses. They tend to be of four years duration, offering a BSc Degree in Environmental Health Science. Essential practical training is gained in placement with a local authority working alongside qualified EHOs. This gives students an opportunity to sample all aspects of the work and gain the 'hands-on' experience necessary to become a qualified EHO professional.

Recruitment: District Councils recruit EHOs by advertising in local papers or in the CIEHs magazine. Job sharing is available in Belfast. Opportunities are also available for EHOs to be employed within the private sector as consultants.

Training: Continual professional development is vital to keep abreast with new legislation and current technical knowledge. This can be achieved by attending seminars, conferences and training courses. Postgraduate courses are available which can lead to an MSc or diploma eg in Health and Safety or the Institute of Acoustics. After graduation and a minimum of two years professional practice an assessment of professional competence can be undertaken. Successful completion enables Corporate Membership of the CIEH.

Consumer Protection: EHOs are concerned with ensuring the safety of food at all stages of production and distribution until it reaches the consumer. They also deal with consumer safety, communicable disease control and poor health duties.

EHOs work to protect the public from environmental health risks. The job is wide ranging: assessing high risk food premises, assessing unfitness in houses, investigating fatal accidents or complaints regarding noisy parties. Academic qualifications alone are not sufficient. EHOs must have a broad technical knowledge but the ability to deal with people and good communication skills are vital.

Profile

Heather Armstrong, 32, joined Belfast City Council in 1985 and is now the Senior EHO (Noise Control) working with the pollution control team.

'I was always interested in environmental issues and strongly favoured science subjects. What attracted me to a career in environmental health was the opportunity to utilise scientific expertise and yet still have direct contact with the public. I worked for five years with the food safety team before moving to pollution control. The work is varied and I enjoy being out and about. Noise Control can involve late night working to monitor sleep disturbance but overtime is paid for these duties. The Council does not provide a 24 hour service but an out of hours call out procedure exists for emergencies. We deal with a wide range of noise complaints – noisy neighbours, barking dogs, construction sites and noise from pubs, clubs and factories. Each complaint presents its own particular problems and investigation requires expertise, professionalism and the use of monitoring and recording equipment. Statutory noise nuisances are dealt with by legal action although many complaints are resolved by informal means. EHOs however do need to deal with situations where their presence is not always welcomed. Since graduating I have had the opportunity to

complete the Institute of Acoustics Diploma in Noise Control and the knowledge gained is of assistance in my daily work.

I am also a member of the Northern Ireland Radiation Monitoring Group. We monitor background radiation levels and sample foods and environmental materials for analysis. This work has evolved considerably since the accident at Chernobyl – prior to that our monitoring tended to focus on the Irish Sea and in particular discharges from Sellafield. However, our work now takes account of airborne contamination of freshwater and terrestrial environments, in addition to the marine environment.

Environmental Health is a living profession, constantly undergoing change in technology, legislation and philosophies. Many environmental pollution problems require a holistic approach and meeting the challenge provides a stimulating and worthwhile career.'

RESEARCH AND MONITORING

LABORATORY OF THE GOVERNMENT CHEMIST
Queens Road, Teddington, Middlesex TW11 0LY

The LGC is one of the largest and most up-to-date chemical science laboratories in Europe, and is equipped with the latest instrumentation. It provides analytical, investigatory and consultancy services and policy support to customers in government, local authorities and the private sector. In 1996, it is intended that the LGC should transfer to the private sector.

LGC's high quality service and impartial advice is based on expertise in chemistry and the biosciences. The scientific work of the laboratory has been divided into five market segments: Environment; Food; Forensic Science; Health and Safety and New Technologies. LGC is in the forefront of a new DTI initiative concerned with Valid Analytical Measurement (VAM). The aim of this initiative is to improve the quality of analytical measurements and to work for a greater degree of harmonisation of these measurements across Europe.

In the area of environmental protection, LGC provides a comprehensive range of consultancy, advisory and analytical services to customers. Services include analysis of hazardous substances in water supplies, waste water and effluents, contaminated land and buildings, marine pollution and pesticide residues in food. Techniques employed include radiochemical analysis and trace element analysis and analytical microbiology.

Typical staff: Graduates & Postgraduates. Scientists, largely chemists and biochemists, biologists and forensic scientists. In addition to further scientific training, staff are sponsored to follow further study and research, including PhD MBA and professional qualifications. Staff are also encouraged to develop their business skills, including project management, marketing and the use of Information Technology.

Non-Graduates. Assistant Scientific Officers (ASOs) who undertake detailed observations through experiments and tests, logging data and collecting samples. Non-graduate staff are encouraged to undertake further studies on a part-time day release basis.

Potential ASOs need a minimum of four GCSEs at grade C or higher and these should include Chemistry, Mathematics and English Language. Equivalent GNVQ/SNVQs are also accepted.

Sandwich and Work Experience Placements: Occasional sandwich placements are offered. LGC also offers unpaid work experience placements to students from pre-GCSE to postgraduate levels. Work shadow placements are also offered.

Likely number of vacancies: Between 10–15 a year, arising throughout the year.

LGC accepts speculative enquiries and has the facility to hold names and addresses.

Recruitment method: Scientific posts are advertised mainly in *New Scientist* and occasionally in the local and national press.

Profiles

Dr Valerie Forster, 33, graduated with a degree in Chemistry and a PhD in Environmental Analytical Chemistry from the University of Southampton, and joined the Mass Spectrometry team at LGC eight years ago.

'My first post involved the analysis of a range of compounds from controlled drugs to dioxins using mass spectrometry. I also oversaw the installation of a new state-of-the-art tandem mass spectrometer and performed initial tests on this instrument. During this period, I was seconded to the DTI Innovation Unit in London to gain experience in developing scientific policy.

On returning to LGC, my next post was concerned with promoting the importance of the DTI's Valid Analytical Measurement (VAM) Initiative to the education sector. This work involved establishing a wide network of contacts with schools, universities and training suppliers.

I have just finished a period of work in environmental consultancy where I carried out a range of desk based projects related to contaminated land and environmental monitoring. During this period I was seconded, on a part-time basis, to the Department of the Environment to manage their Contaminated Land Research Programme.

Recently I moved to a new position within the Business Development and Marketing Group of LGC. As a Business Development Manager for environmental services, I have wide-ranging responsibilities for expanding our business in this area.'

Miss Jo Peet, 25, graduated with a degree in Chemistry and Geography from St Mary's College, University of Surrey, four years ago and joined the Safety, Air, Land & Water section of LGC.

'At that time I was instrumental in the expansion of the section to form LGC's Contaminated Land Unit. I have since managed a variety of land investigations, which include former factories, gas works and other former industrial sites.

I have also qualified in Occupational Health and Safety with LGC sponsorship, and work on a variety of safety related projects including the investigation of Sick Building syndrome and Chemical Decontamination work.

I am now an Environmental Consultant with LGC, specializing in the investigation of contaminated land and water. My work includes the design of site investigations, the interpretation of site data and analytical results and the advisory aspects of land and water investigations, particularly those for Local Authorities and Government Departments. A large proportion of my time is spent away from the laboratory visiting clients and supervising site work.

I am also conducting a research assessment into the viability of on-site monitors and test kits, that are used in contaminated land and water investigations.

The variety and scope of the environmental investigations that I am involved with makes my job both interesting and challenging.'

THE NATURAL ENVIRONMENT RESEARCH COUNCIL Polaris House, North Star Avenue, Swindon SN2 1UE

The Natural Environment Research Council (NERC) spans the whole spectrum of scientific research on the environment. Its mission is to advance understanding of the natural environment and the processes of environmental change. A key strength is its unique ability to support multi-disciplinary research and promote an integrated approach to projects.

Through its research findings NERC gives impartial advice to government, industry and society as a whole to help formulate sound environmental policies. Their continued research adds to our knowledge of climate change, acid rain and the depletion of the ozone layer.

NERC's research activities are divided between its own research institutes and universities throughout the UK. Most research programmes fall into three main Science Directorates: Earth; Marine and Atmospheric; and Terrestrial and Freshwater. The British Antarctic Survey also forms part of NERC.

The global nature of many of the environmental problems facing the world today means research is often on an international scale providing opportunities for travel abroad.

NERC has over 2,100 permanent employees and another 800 undertaking special projects on contracts of from three to five years. It also provides grants for fellowships and studentships covering the entire range of environmental sciences.

In a typical year NERC gives 300 research PhD studentships (lasting up to three years), 200 advanced course MSc studentships (lasting a year), and around 20 post-doctoral fellowships (lasting up to five years), plus about 100 research grants.

Typical staff: Graduate scientists – BSc and PhD (1,500 approximately). Range of disciplines depending on institution and research programme. Technical engineering staff – HNC and HND (250 approx) to make specialist equipment for scientists. Contract staff to man research vessel for Antarctic exploration (270 approx).

Recruitment method: Technical and specialist press: *New Scientist, Nature*. Quality national newspapers. Local press for Engineering Staff.

Training: Where required for specialist projects.

Likely number of vacancies: Varies, depending on Institute.

Work experience: Occasionally industrial opportunities for sandwich students within different Institutions.

Profile

Eleanor Blyth, 30, graduated from Cambridge with a degree in General Engineering and worked for Hydraulics Research Ltd in Wallingford, Oxfordshire for 3½ years. She has since moved to the NERC Institute of Hydrology, also in Wallingford, where she is engaged in research work that will form the basis for a PhD.

'I came out of university wanting to do overseas work, helping third world countries. I saw myself digging wells in Africa. That's why I originally joined Hydraulics Research.

But involvement with two major environmental projects to do with soil erosion changed the course of my career.

One project was for the Philippines where their reservoirs were becoming silted up, and they wanted to know if the cause could be deforestation. The other was in Botswana where we were looking to see why the vegetation was unable to hold the soil down and it was getting washed away.

The environment as a topic is intellectually very stimulating because it is so difficult and so important. When I was offered the chance by NERC to undertake a project to improve the global computer models used for global warming prediction, I was more than interested.

Computer models existed to calculate evaporation from land surfaces that were completely uniform – such as all trees or all grass land – but they wanted a model that could predict evaporation from a mixed surface so they can predict more accurately how much global warming is affecting temperatures. It was something that had never been done before, which has to be challenging.'

SILSOE RESEARCH INSTITUTE Wrest Park, Silsoe, Bedford MK45 4HS

One of the seven institutes of the Biotechnology and Biological Sciences Research Council, the Silsoe Research Institute specialises in engineering science as applied to the agricultural, horticultural, forestry, aquacultural, crop processing, food processing and rural amenities industries.

Major aspects of the Institute's current programme include strategic research on image analysis from remote sensing, robotic harvesting, information transfer, slurry handling and storage, and emission reduction. It is renowned worldwide for its research and vehicle testing activities.

The Institute's aim is to contribute to the public good through efficient, high quality food production, and by safeguarding the rural environment and the health of farm workers and animals. So therefore, much of its work is environmentally based.

More specific environmental research topics currently under investigation include: reducing emissions and odours from slurry storage and its application to the land; minimising applications of agricultural chemicals, such as in sprays and fertilisers; reducing drift from agricultural sprays; reducing silage effluent production; reducing aerial pollutants from animal housing; reducing environmental noise; soil management, and agricultural and rural development in developing countries.

Number of employees: 280, of whom 180 are in scientific posts.

Typical staff: Researchers with expertise in mechanical, chemical and vehicle engineering, environmental physics, materials science, ergonomics, information technology, control engineering, robotics.

Qualifications: For scientific posts: a first class or upper second class BSc; or lower second plus MSc and PhD. Occasionally lower level degrees, HNC or HND are accepted. Current recruitment is mostly at a high level and most recruits have a PhD.

Recruitment methods: Initially trawl within the Biotechnology and Biological Sciences Research Council, then advertise externally in technical press such as *New Scientist* and national press. Local press used for industrial and secretarial vacancies.

Likely number of vacancies: Six plus per year.

Training: Given individually when required.

Profile

Dr Roger Phillips, joined the Silsoe Research Institute 12 years ago to lead a group working on pollution problems associated with livestock waste. He has a BSc from Cambridge and a PhD gained in Canada in Chemical Engineering.

'I knew nothing about agriculture before I came here. I was in the nuclear industry, working on the development of fuels for fast breeder reactors at Harwell. Hardly, you might think, a suitable background but . . .

We have recently won a prize for a slurry spreading device we developed, based on an idea which I came across during my nuclear days. Hopefully now it will go into production.

Right from the start I could see the job would be a chance to be right at the sharp end of helping the environment. We look at the handling and treatment of farm waste with the overall objective of reducing its impact on the environment. The challenge, however, is not just to find ways to cut down water pollution and smells, but to develop methods where the costs are not too excessive for the farmer to bear.

Currently I have five major research projects on the go. These are all centred around the problem of pollutants released from livestock housing. In the UK, for example, livestock wastes are the major source of ammonia emissions and these are implicated in the problems of forest die-back and nutrient excesses in the soil and water which upset natural ecosystems. We are measuring the emissions of pollutants like methane, ammonia and nitrous oxide from livestock buildings and researching methods of reducing them. I am also helping to compile a comprehensive UK inventory of the gases released from livestock housing.

We collaborate with universities and other institutes in the UK and abroad – Holland in particular – which brings an added dimension to our work and, occasionally, trips overseas.'

NON-GOVERNMENTAL ORGANISATIONS

GREENPEACE Canonbury Villas, London N1 2PN

Hardly a week goes by without Greenpeace being in the news. Since 1971 they have been at the forefront of the fight to protect the natural

Number of employees: 90 approximately.

Typical staff: Campaigners (43) with specialist knowledge and campaign expertise, including scientists, media officers, investigators, political lobbyists, actions and communications staff.

Fund Raisers (18) using direct mail techniques and organising nationwide collections and sponsored events through a network of local groups

Information staff (6) producing and distributing magazines, briefings, leaflets etc for businesses and supporters, and answering the public's written and telephone queries.

Finance, legal, office management, IT, volunteer management and personnel staff (23).

Greenpeace depend greatly on volunteers in all areas of work, and from time to time create placements suitable for people on Training for Work and other work experience schemes (minimum three months). Contact the Volunteer and Placement Manager for more information.

Staff for Greenpeace ships are hired by Greenpeace International Marine Services – address available from Personnel.

Qualifications: Only required where relevant to a particular post. University degrees, therefore, are not necessary for most jobs. However, relevant experience and knowledge is nearly always required.

Recruitment method: CVs are not accepted. Vacancies are advertised in *The Guardian*, specialist publications where relevant, jobcentres and *The Voice/The Weekly Journal*. Greenpeace is an equal opportunities employer and treats all applications on merit. Contact Personnel for more information.

Number of vacancies: A few per year.

world from environmental abuse. Through the lobbying of national and international governing bodies, the publication of scientific studies and direct action aimed at the culprits, Greenpeace has brought environmental degradation to people's attention.

As an international, independent pressure group, campaigns are based on what is best for the environment to protect it from harmful interference and they will never compromise this position.

Their main concerns are the direct threat to wildlife through pollution and habitat loss and the dangers caused by the production and release of radioactive materials and toxic waste into the environment. Major campaigns have been launched to save the whales, stop nuclear weapons testing, stop the dumping of radio-active waste and dangerous chemicals at sea, stop global warming and protect the atmosphere from ozone destruction.

THE ROYAL SOCIETY FOR THE PROTECTION OF BIRDS
The Lodge, Sandy, Bedfordshire, SG19 2DL

The RSPB exists to conserve wild birds and the environment in which they live. It buys up land to create nature reserves which it then runs.

Currently it has 129 reserves located throughout the UK, ranging in size. This totals 83,500 hectares altogether, over twice the size of the Isle of Wight.

While its main function is protecting and improving the habitat for wildlife, the RSPB also gets involved in campaigns to oppose developments which threaten the environment: in lobbying Parliament to introduce laws to protect species; in advising landowners and planners on environmental issues; in carrying out research into many aspects of nature conservation; and by playing a major role in educating young people.

With a staff of some 680 plus around 2,000 volunteers per year, the RSPB is one of the largest environmental employers, though not all jobs could be strictly termed 'conservation'.

Typical staff: Warden: 75 established staff plus approx 100 contract staff engaged on assignments which run between four and 24 months. Wardens help run the reserves, are engaged in a range of physical tasks such as thinning scrub, cutting reeds, cleaning ditches, building hides and dealing with the public. **Qualifications**: degree, ideally in a natural history-based discipline such as biology, ecology, zoology, environmental sciences or botany; with strong ornithological interest.

Research Assistant/Biologist: mainly temporary posts – three months to three years – for survey work, ecological studies, species studies. Around 30 per year. Degree in biology/zoology with some training in statistics and computing. PhD or MSc often required.

Conservation: good ornithological experience plus knowledge of ecology and land use.

Species protection: usually temporary. Legal plus ornithological knowledge.

Teacher/naturalist: based at reserves to take school parties round. Degree in science discipline plus suitable teaching experience.

Public Affairs ensures that the Society communicates messages which enhance its corporate identity. Main areas of work are:

Publishing – producing publications and exhibition material – editing, design or print buying background desirable.

The Campaigns Unit – works with Conservation and Marketing to ensure that messages on specific conservation issues are communicated to the right audience, at the best time and in the most effective way. Influencing skills, plus tact and diplomacy.

The Press Office – communicates through the media, influencing public opinion in favour of conservation. Therefore a journalistic or a PR background is required.

The Events Section – provided an efficient, value-for-money event management service. Good organisational skills essential.

The Photographic and Film & Video Unit – provides a

cost-effective, professional service, producing visual resources. Experience in filming, editing, production could be beneficial.

The Library – provides a central information and general reference service, holding more than 9,000 books and periodicals.

Marketing: people to organise fund raising events, contact companies and individuals for donations, and increase membership. Experience of fund raising or marketing.

Administration: secretaries, finance, computer systems and other office personnel.

Youth and Volunteers looks after the Young Ornithologists' Club (YOC), the junior membership of the RSPB. Also co-ordinates and provde support for the volunteers that help the RSPB in a wide range of tasks.

Education – each year we develop and produce a number of curriculum guides, educational policy documents and termly newsletters that cater for all school age ranges. Previous teaching experience an advantage.

Recruitment method: *The Guardian*. Specialist press: *New Scientist, Birds* magazine. Occasionally local press.

Number of staff recruited: Varies. Wide range of voluntary work available.

Profile

Peter Bradley, 34, is a Warden at Surlingham and Rockland Reserve in Norfolk. He graduated in Accountancy at Kent University, and trained as an accountant for six years before joining the RSPB as a volunteer six years ago.

'I suddenly woke up and thought, do I really want to be an accountant for the rest of my life? When I realized the answer was 'no', I decided to work as a volunteer on an RSPB reserve for a month. It would change

the pace of my life, I thought. In fact it was the turning point in my career.

Who could not be enchanted by the open marsh lands, the wildfowl, the Caledonian pine forests and mountains of Scotland?

Accommodation was an isolated house up a muddy track, with no electricity – and if you wanted to keep warm you had to chop logs. It was quite an experience.

Eighteen months later I became a temporary warden at Nags Head Reserve in the Forest of Dean. It was only a 4½-month contract but it was a foot in the right door.

Monitoring pied flycatchers for a major research programme and maintaining and cleaning the 360 nesting boxes, repairing fences, gate hanging, damming streams, ensuring only the right scrub land grew, grazing sheep, talking to the public, guided tours – that was my job from now on.

As a warden it's a whole different ball game. You are in charge, you make the decisions. It's your job to build up a rapport with the local community, to influence public opinion, and try to persuade people to manage their land better. The job of conservation is very far reaching.

It's hard work: I was up at five; I took a cut in salary. It's chucking it down outside right now, but no, I've no regrets about changing careers.'

WWF-UK, WORLD WIDE FUND FOR NATURE, Panda House, Weyside Park, Godalming, Surrey GU7 1XR

WWF-UK is one of 28 national organisations in the WWF international family and is based at Godalming in Surrey. Like its counterparts worldwide, it has three goals: to preserve the extraordinary variety and range of life on earth; to use renewable natural resources like water and timber in sustainable ways; and to reduce to a minimum pollution and the wasteful consumption of energy.

The global issues that concern WWF include the damage being done to the world's forests; pollution of our rivers, seas, land and the air we breathe; the menace of global warming; the human population explosion; the exploitation of endangered species; and the over-use of natural resources (such as oil).

These broad issues are mirrored at home – which is why WWF takes the lead in environmental education in our schools and colleges, and why it spends some £4 million a year on home projects alone.

Profile

Francis Sullivan, 32, is Forest Conservation Officer with WWF UK. He joined them eight years ago with a BA in Agricultural and Forestry Science and an MSc in Forestry and Land Use, both from Oxford.

Number of staff employed: 200 in the UK.

Recruitment methods: *The Guardian*, specialist, technical and local press.

'My interest in environmental work developed out of a year I spent in Thailand whilst at university. The scale of devastation, and the poverty of the people, opened my eyes to the realities of a very real crisis which could not be ignored. It made me want to get into overseas conservation.

I cut my teeth with WWF on the Korup region of Cameroon, where we were setting up a rainforest national park project. I then moved across the border to Nigeria and the Cross River national park project.

While individual projects were successful, it was becoming increasingly obvious there was a need in WWF for people to look at things on a larger scale, and to target those who had influence on the fate of the forests – governments and industry – so my job became one of lobbying and campaigning linked to project work overseas. My aim is to encourage industry and government to improve their policies towards forests, and in doing so to look at projects which will have an impact on forest degradation – things like mining, road building, agriculture. In other words, to get industry and government to preserve our forests, wherever they may be.

I also try to encourage aid agencies such as the Overseas Development Administration to think about environmental issues and put their funds into projects similar to ours, while reducing the environmental impact of projects they fund in the developing world. It's all to do with aid and trade. So I'm not so much a field man but a policy lobbyist.

My job requires a lot of travel. Recently I was in New York at the Commission for Sustainable Development, pushing for governments to act on the commitments they have made to conserve the world's forests. I must have worked in 20 countries over the last five years. You can't just focus on environmental problems in your own country, because it's a multi-national problem, as the Earth Summit underlined. The trouble is everybody thinks it's someone else who is causing the problems. In Brazil they say it's not the devastation of the Amazon rainforest but car drivers in North America who are contributing to global warming. In Britain we think it's the rainforest destruction not the acid rain.

I work closely with industry, and have set up the WWF 1995 Group – a partnership between WWF and over 50 British companies which have pledged themselves to phase out the use of unsustainable wood by the end of 1995. It's very important to get this sort of good news out to a public audience, so I write a lot for the Timber Trades Journal and BBC Wildlife magazine – they are my main mouthpieces.

Soon we will help launch a new timber labelling scheme, called the Forest Stewardship Council. A new breed of logo will shortly appear – one which the consumer can trust because it's based on independent verification of every forest.

This means we can now put a finger on how fast our forests are disappearing and we can show just how urgent things are. At the current rate of forest loss, there will be nothing left in the tropics in 30 years and life on earth really would come to an end. I think there's enough evidence to show that. So this is not something we can ignore. That's what drives me on.'

RETAIL/DISTRIBUTIVE COMPANIES

THE BODY SHOP Hawthorn Road, Wick, Littlehampton, West Sussex BN17 7LR

The Body Shop takes a rather different approach from retailers like Tesco and Sainsbury. Its whole operation is founded on the use of naturally based products. Since the first shop was opened 16 years ago, the organisation has grown to more than 800 stores around the world stretching from the Arctic to Australia, from Jeddah to Japan. It trades in 41 countries and 19 different languages, and sells over 350 different products.

The company has a high environmental campaigning profile and is against testing on animals. Products are often sourced from the Third World, i.e. the developing countries. Its roving anthropologists travel the world to discover the skin and hair care secrets of other cultures. Over half of all products are manufactured in-house, the rest by outside suppliers. A team of some 20 research and development scientists and another 20 quality control specialists ensure all products meet the Body Shop's high environmental standards.

While environmental responsibility has been devolved down into the business with every shop and department having its designated member of staff responsible for the environment on a part-time basis, environmental activities and policy throughout the company are developed by the Environment, Health and Safety Department which comprises a team of eight people based at head office in Littlehampton. A number of campaigns, and a proposed plan to set up a wind farm to create electricity were initiated by this department. For many of its campaigns such as save the rain forest and save the whale, it works closely with the Communications Department and the Design Studio.

The company has its own Community Projects Department which takes action on a range of issues connected with the environment in its widest sense: for example, all employees get half a day off each month to participate in some community activity.

While staff such as designers, journalists in Communications, and scientists taken on in Research and Development and Quality Control, are expected to have a strong commitment to the environment, they will need to have the relevant qualifications for the job.

Only those taken into the Environment, Health and Safety Department will need environment-related qualifications.

Typical staff: Environmental auditors in the Ethical Audit Department, environmental and health and safety managers in operational divisions and coordinators overseeing the retail market on environmental issues. Ethical Audit also employs an administrator, personal assistant, and ethical (environmental) trainer.

Designers: 20–25, based in London, produce leaflets, brochures and posters to support the company's products and campaigns. They often have an environmental track record and should know the most environmentally benign printing materials.

Communications: journalists, PR and communciations professionals with environmental and social commitment.

Research and Development and Quality Control: typical scientific disciplines: chemists, biologists, microbiologists.

Likely vacancies: Few.

Recruitment methods: National press, professional and technical magazines, local press, job centres, employment agencies, speculative applications, head hunting.

Profile

David Wheeler, 35, joined The Body Shop a year ago as General Manager of their Environment, Health and Safety Department. He has a BSc in Microbiology and a PhD in Water Quality and Health from Surrey University. Prior to this job he spent four years in the water industry, eight years in water and sanitation research and development at Surrey University and a year as a scientific adviser on environmental issues to a Member of Parliament.

'When I saw this job advertised it appealed to me. The Body Shop is an environmentally switched on organisation. It's a company that wants to make a difference at a practical level. I had been working on the environmental policy side for a few years – it was nice to be at the sharp end and in a position to stimulate action.

As General Manager of the Environmental Department my job is to make sure we actually do practise what we preach. For us it's not enough to say "wouldn't it be nice to save the ozone layer or tackle global warming", we try to do something, hence our plans to set up a wind farm.

It was a discussion I had with our Dutch director, on being energy self-sufficient down here in Littlehampton, which sparked off the idea. It will be a major project – 24 turbines situated on a Welsh hillside, feeding renewable energy into the national grid. Things do happen.

Take another example: we try and cut down as much as possible on the use of packaging. The result: our unique bottle refilling scheme now established throughout our shops.

Internally my job is environmental management throughout the business in the UK and abroad. Externally it involves liaison with environmental organisations, with policy makers and with industry. I give a lot of talks. We don't heckle industry – we just say "this is what we are doing, isn't it easy, why don't you do the same?"

Working closely with our Communications Department, I also play a role in developing campaigns, for which The Body Shop is well known.

My interest in the environment has grown steadily from my first job in the water industry through my years in R and D (research and development) at Surrey University. My year as a scientific adviser on the environment to a Member of Parliament opened my eyes to how much needed to be done. At the Body Shop we do it, which is very satisfying.'

CORPORATE

BRITISH AIRWAYS PLC Speedbird House, PO Box 10, Heathrow Airport, Hounslow, Middx, TW6 2JA

British Airways is the world's largest international passenger airline employing some 50,000 people worldwide. With 291,000 flights in 1993/94, the airline's fleet carried more than 30 million passengers and 600,000 tonnes of cargo to 165 scheduled destinations in 75 countries.

British Airways has a long standing involvement with environment and community, eg the recycling of tyres and waste oils by the Engineering Department and the recently celebrated ten years of Assisting Nature Conservation. The growing importance of the environment as a focus for management at British Airways was formally recognised by the appointment of a Director of Safety, Security and Environment in 1989. This was followed shortly afterwards by the appointment of Head of the Environment. The Corporate Environment Branch now comprises five full-time staff with the objective to advise, support, promote and stimulate improved environmental performance throughout the company. The Corporate Team is supported by a number of full-time and part-time staff in line departments.

As part of the overall environmental programme, British Airways developed a corporate 'Good Neighbour' goal, 'to be a good neighbour concerned for the community and the environment'. This broad goal is supported by a more detailed Environmental Policy and an extensive programme addressing the key issues.

Typical staff: Graduates and postgraduates in environmental sciences, chemistry or geography. Some openings for tourism and travel specialists.

Number of openings: Occasional.

Recruitment method: To date mainly by internal advertising. One position in a line department has been filled using specialist press.

Profile

Gary Meades, 35, has been Manager of Environment at British Airways for three years. He has a BSc in Environmental Studies from the University of Hertfordshire, an MSc in Environmental Pollution Sciences from Brunel University and an MBA from Lancaster University.

'I have been interested in environmental issues since I was a teenager so it was natural that I would study the subject at University. By the time I had finished my degree course and spent a years placement with the Environment Branch of the then Central Electricity Generating Board, I was certain that I wanted to work in industry.

I spent the first four years working with the environmental consultancy of a large construction company. During this time I was exposed to safety and occupational hygiene issues. I particularly liked the human interaction aspects of this work.

I joined British Airways in 1985 as Environmental Adviser in the Safety Department working mainly on occupational hygiene issues. During my six year stay with the Safety Department I branched out into safety management work, helping to develop a new safety management system within the company including a safety auditing protocol.

By this time the work of the newly formed Environment Branch had expanded and I joined the Environment Branch in 1993 to strengthen the technical experience of the team and work specifically on compliance issues.

It was good to get back to environmental concerns. It took me some time to catch up with the large changes that had occurred since the last time I had dealt with these issues.

I now deal with the compliance issues of air emissions, noise, waste, aqueous effluent and land contamination. I am particularly interested in environmental management systems, environmental reporting and environmental auditing. Last year I co-produced the British Airways Annual Environment Report and I have recently become an accredited Environmental Auditor under the EARA scheme.

It is very rewarding working for a company who is committed to responsible environmental management and a constant challenge trying to maintain the company's prominent position as an industry leader in this area'.

EDUCATION AND TRAINING

TEACHING

The avalanche of interest among students and employers in environmental issues has resulted in the proliferation of Environmental Science courses at universities throughout the country. One of the growing environmental career areas is therefore in teaching. Who are the lecturers on these courses? Where have they come from? What are they trying to achieve?

Profile

Dr Stephen John Edwards, 31, is a Senior Lecturer in Environmental Geochemistry and Course Leader of the BSc (Honours) degree in Environmental Science in the Department of Environmental and Geographical Sciences at the **Manchester Metropolitan University**; here he talks about his career and the degree which he coordinates.

'From a young age my career ambition was to become a university lecturer actively involved in research. I read Geochemistry at London University because of my interest in the earth sciences and chemistry. On graduation I was awarded a postgraduate fellowship and Commonwealth Scholarship to research my PhD at Memorial University of Newfoundland, Canada. My project was a field, geochemical and mineralogical investigation of magmatic and fluid processes in the earth's mantle that lead to the formation of oceanic crust and certain ore deposits. The Geological Survey of Canada was interested in my work and awarded me several applied research contracts. On completion of my PhD I had a short period of post-doctoral research at Memorial before moving to Manchester.

Why, you might ask, as a geochemist, did I chose to move to an environmental discipline? The answer is that it is not a move. Geochemistry is the study of the distribution, abundance and behaviour of chemical species in earth and planetary systems. These systems are a major and vital component of our whole environment, which has developed over the last 4.6 billion years since the formation of the earth. Environmental geochemistry investigates the interactions and responses of humans to the distribution and interrelations of chemical species and radioactivity in the whole environment. I firmly believe that it is essential to understand the 'natural' environment before human impact on the environment can be determined. Take, for example, global warming: the geological record preserves evidence for numerous periods of global warming and cooling. The question we have to address today is whether human activity is causing global warming and, if so, is the effect significant?'

The course
'You could argue Environmental Science is one of the most difficult degrees because you have to have a good grasp of four or five scientific disciplines as well as an understanding of economics and socio-political issues. Our Environmental Science degree provides students with this background by integrating field and laboratory work with lectures, seminars and tutorials. In addition, vocational projects and placements involve students with external clients and organisations. The broad applied nature of this degree is attractive to employers in industry, commerce, business and academia.

Demand for the course remains stable and high. The course is continually updated and overseas links increase every year. Overall, there is a very bright and exciting future for the course which should appeal to young and mature students alike. The broad, applied nature of the degree is attractive to employers.'

4 CHOOSING A COURSE

This chapter, together with the course listings in Appendix II on page 111 provides a guide to degree and postgraduate courses in the UK. Given that the number of environmental courses has increased significantly over the last few years, with new courses being added on an annual basis, it is inevitable that the course listings in Appendix II are not an exhaustive list. That said the courses which are included in this edition of the handbook are representative of the wide spectrum of provision.

The intention of the Institution of Environmental Sciences' survey of universities and colleges, on which the course listings are based, was to identify courses which are explicitly *interdisciplinary* and *applied* and therefore are able to provide graduates with the skills necessary for practise as an environmental professional.

In the previous edition of this Handbook it was noted that the term 'environmental' had increasingly been used as an umbrella term to describe a range of specialised courses. In the last few years the range of courses which are labelled environmental has increased significantly. Examples here include, amongst others, environmental chemistry, environmental physics, environmental biology and environmental engineering/technology. It is also the case that a number of courses adopting a more social scientific stance have been

introduced under the heading of 'environmental studies'. In this category it is possible to identify courses such as urban and environmental studies, environmental planning, environmental management and environmental and social values.

It is not possible to make a clear distinction between courses described by individual institutions as environmental science or environmental studies. However, in general the former are character-ised by degree programmes which have a clearly identified scientific strand but which incorporate a social science/policy dimension whereas the latter focus more overtly on policy issues and the social, economic and philosophical debates which surround the environment.

It is not appropriate here to consider individually the courses included in the appendix of courses on page 111, nor to attempt to categorise them or place them on an environmental science/studies continuum. Such a task is most effectively undertaken by an applicant seeking admission to the course. The purpose of this introduction is to alert those seeking to pursue an environmental course to the questions which could usefully inform their decision to select one course over another.

What follows then are a series of pointers to assist a would be applicant in evaluating the extent to which a particular course of study will meet individual aspirations in the context of both an educational experience and future career plans.

EMPLOYMENT AND EMPLOYER DEMAND

It is certainly the case that the number of graduates in environmental sciences/studies appears to exceed employment opportunities if the yardstick is taken as the number of graduates from these disciplines whose first job is directly related to their studies. Applicants must therefore have a clear view of their reasons for pursuing an environmental course at university. For example, the candidate who is ultimately seeking employment in an environmental consultancy, where there is a need for strongly developed scientific and quanti-tative skills, is unlikely to find himself/herself well served by taking a programme of study which has little or no practical content. It is important to reiterate here that the *title* of a degree programme may not always fully reflect its *content*. Therefore, the overriding message is for candidates to have realistic expectations of their course of study and its limitations, how their pre-university education and experience has equipped them for higher education and what is their chosen end point.

The academic content of a degree is, of course, of vital importance. However, it is increasingly the case that employers, in addition to recruiting from a pool of graduates who share a set of academic and technical skills, also have regard to the extent to which potential employees have developed a repertoire of what are referred to as **'transferable skills'**. These latter skills include amongst others computer literacy, communication skills and possession of a second language . For this reason applicants should investigate the extent to which information technology, presentational skills and the opportunity to study a foreign language are built into their programme of study. It goes without saying that environmental practitioners are heavily involved in field assessments and the proportion of field based to theoretical work should be carefully considered. It is unlikely that a graduate who has been exposed to a limited amount of field work would possess the skills mix which many employers in the environmental field find a prerequisite to employment. Therefore, in selecting his/her course a candidate may look to the incorporation of a sandwich year (a year of related employment after two years of study) as well as the existence of international exchange links. It is increasingly the case that students can spend a period of time in another European university.

ACADEMIC CONSIDERATIONS

Turning now to the academic content of environmental programmes. As previously stated, it is not intended here to review exhaustively specific courses; in the final analysis it is a matter of personal choice which course a candidate selects. However, given the array of courses on offer it is important to consider what features a candidate should look for in drawing up a shortlist and making a final selection.

The first consideration must be to look at what can perhaps be identified as the specific/generalist distinction. Is the course predominantly a single science degree which merely employs environmental examples or is the course one with a strong social science/ geographical and/or management focus? Alternatively, does the course present a balance between the natural and social sciences thus presenting the holistic approach which is arguably the basis of the discipline of environmental science?

Since in many cases a candidate's first knowledge of a university's programmes of study will be from published material it is important to extract key information. In particular an applicant should consider the following:

Composition of the course team. What are the academic and research skills of the teaching team? This information will be available from both the institutional prospectus and individual departmental course details. While such documentation provides an initial basis for selection it is likely, however, that candidates will want to visit a small number of institutions whose provision looks to meet their educational and career aspirations.

If the course is clearly identified as being multidisciplinary is the academic team associated with it multidisciplinary or does it appear that there is a disciplinary bias? A preponderance of say chemists or biologists is inevitable if the course is stated as being explicitly environmental chemistry or environmental biology for example, but a careful analysis of this kind of information may prevent later disappointment. A multidisciplinary course needs a multidisciplinary team so ask the right questions at an early stage.

Research and Consultancy. The extent to which the teaching is underpinned by research and consultancy is an important element. Are the academic staff actively involved with environmental research and consultancy? It is important that you have an opportunity to discuss contemporary issues in the context of real world case studies and what better source than those who are teaching you being able to illustrate their teaching programme with source material from their own experience. Sandwich placement opportunities or undergraduate projects also develop from academic staff contacts.

Library provision. Look at the library provision which supports the course and don't just look at the library shelves.The literature which will add significantly to your studies changes rapidly and you will need to have access to a range of journals so look at those available. Check on whether students have access to inter-library loan facilities and what your library borrowing rights will be. What are the opening hours of the library? Can you study in the library, in the evenings and at the weekends?

Increasingly texts and other data are stored on CDs and other forms of electronic retrieval systems. Check with the library staff the extent of this kind of provision and again what access would you have to this as a student.

Finally, the acquisition of computing skills is increasingly important for your future career. What access do students have to computing facilities in the institution and what range of software is available. Do students for example have an e-mail facility?

Laboratory provision. The environmental sciences are undeniably laboratory based and you should look carefully at laboratory provision. When you visit your shortlist of universities ask about laboratories and ensure that you go on a tour. Don't just be impressed by a lot of high tech equipment. Ask about it and whether you will get to use it, or is it reserved for research staff? Remember that for those who intend to go on to consultancy or field based work you will be at an advantage if you have 'hands on experience'.

Open days. Attendance at open days is an important feature of choosing your course. It is during your visit that you will be able to ask some or all of the questions outlined above and don't forget that your questions are not all for the academic staff. Make sure that during your visit you speak to technical, library and administrative staff. They will all contribute to your experience while at university and are just as important as the lecturing staff. Perhaps one aspect of the acid test is to ask current students their views.

From the above you will see that your choice of a course goes far beyond just its content, although no doubt this will be your major consideration. Studying for a degree is more than acquiring facts and passing examinations; you need to evaluate the strengths and weaknesses of individual institutions and the opportunities you will have to develop the skills you will need as an environmental scientist. You are not, however, totally reliant on your own efforts. Degree courses are now subject to quality assessment procedures. In essence this involves a team of specialist assessors carrying out an indepth evaluation of individual courses, the quality of teaching, course management and facilities to support courses. The results of these assessments are published by the Higher Education Funding Council and will give you a totally objective view of the quality of a university's provision. In particular look for those universities which have been assessed as excellent, the highest category of provision.

POSTGRADUATE PROVISION

While the emphasis of this chapter has been on the selection of an undergraduate course, the advice is equally applicable at postgraduate level.

There has been a significant increase in the number of postgraduate courses in the environmental field both in full and part-time modes. While some of these could be said to be multidisciplinary the majority provide a more in-depth treatment of a specific aspect of, for example, environmental monitoring, conservation or management.

Given the breadth of undergraduate courses there is evidence that graduates are increasingly using the postgraduate route to obtain a first appointment with graduates who have studied single discipline subjects taking advantage of either an MA or MSc to broaden their knowledge and skills base.

Please refer to the appendix of courses on page 111 for a list of undergraduate and postgraduate courses.

5   GETTING A JOB

INTRODUCTION

The current social and political interest in our global environment has contributed to a greater environmental awareness in the population as a whole and in prospective job seekers in particular. In the last few years there has been a dramatic increase in the number of opportunities in the 'environmental' job market. However, the number of people looking for jobs and careers in this sector has also increased and, in some disciplines, has become extremely competitive.

This chapter outlines what to do about deciding on a job, where to look for the job and some tips on application procedures. While this is intended to be a comprehensive outline of the options, there will still be people who may succeed without doing anything mentioned here or who may even be without the skills or experience normally required. But these are usually exceptions; for the great majority the observations and suggestions mentioned here will greatly improve their chances. What is recommended is that if you really do want an environmental job or career then you need to do what it takes to get it. Reading this chapter should remove some of the pain from the process.

Before you begin the business of getting a job you should have some idea of what it is you are thinking of applying for. You may be set on pollution control work, water management or environmental consultancy work or some aspect of conservation or land management. On the other hand, you may not have a precise idea of what it is you want, other than a vague leaning towards environmental work. This chapter will not help with the decision-making process and information search needed to choose a specific occupation. If you need help with this you should use a careers service, either by consulting a careers adviser or by making use of one of a number of careers guidance aids usually available in careers offices.

AN ENVIRONMENTAL JOB OR A GREEN WAY OF LIFE?

Environmental careers cover an extremely wide variety of jobs which have been described elsewhere in this handbook and will not be mentioned specifically in this chapter. They fall into three broad categories:

- influencing environmental change through education, campaigning, political action and policy making

- working in the environment, for example, working as an education officer at a field centre, or environmental monitoring, conservation management, research, warden of a nature reserve or a ranger

- influencing others through your example in which case any job can provide opportunities to act in a 'green' way.

It is important for you, as the prospective job seeker, to decide which of these you wish to follow. Most environmental jobs are rarely glamorous, highly paid or lead to positions of great power and authority. If you wish for these, then look at other careers and decide to help change and improve things in the environment by practising a caring lifestyle and by influencing others in your chosen career at the appropriate times.

Those of you who remain determined to pursue a career in some aspect of environmental work should accept from the outset that it will be competitive and to be successful will require patience, persistence and competence.

WHAT MAKES A GOOD CANDIDATE?

As you will have gathered from the other sections of this handbook the range of employers and types of work are wide. However, most employers look for similar evidence of suitability to do the job. The following are some of the things you should consider:

Qualifications

Many employers consider that an ideal candidate should have good basic science qualifications. This is usually a degree or its equivalent. Suitable subjects include agriculture, biology, microbiology, zoology, plant science, chemistry, physics, engineering, surveying, geology, geography and some others. There has been a general comment from many employers that multi-disciplinary environmental science qualifications as a first degree are not particularly helpful. Those of you who have this type of qualification should take particular care when choosing a postgraduate qualification, and should also remember to highlight the relevant parts of your course in your application.

Postgraduate qualifications which are particularly concerned with the environment have become more valuable and are often requested by employers. These would include PhDs (especially if they are environmentally biased and include technical expertise), vocational taught course MScs and some research MPhil degrees if they are relevant. A number of diploma courses are also available and are increasingly relevant. If you are considering a post-graduate qualification it is worth spending some time to find the right course. Refer to the courses mentioned in this handbook but do follow up and make the right choice. It is worth taking the time to find out what the course involves, what you will get out of it and, equally important, what sort of jobs past students of the course have moved into. In recent times funding has been a problem for many people and is an important factor which will need to be considered when choosing a course. (See the reference section at the back of the book for further sources of information.)

Most of the main environmental organisations have an interest in providing environmental education support for teachers in schools and youth out of school. Some have education departments, others an education officer. Education staff are usually chosen from practising teachers or youth workers. Geography and science are the two main subject disciplines the staff are drawn from. It can help to choose a PGCE course which includes environmental education.

Knowledge to do the job

This factor will be closely related to qualifications in recent school leavers, graduates and those with diplomas but less so in mature students and experienced post-graduates who will often have gained their knowledge from a variety of sources. The basic 'know how' may involve fairly technical laboratory-based procedures, it may be part of a vocational qualification such as town planning, or it may combine technical and scientific knowledge together with commercial experience or writing skills. You will need to look carefully at the job for which you are applying, making sure that you are able to do the job and that you don't forget to mention this in your application.

Commitment and enthusiasm for the environment

It is usually important to provide an employer with evidence of your commitment and enthusiasm. This can be in the form of involvement in a local conservation trust or environmental action group or as a member of certain environmental charities and pressure groups. You should be able to describe to an employer what you have contributed to such a group. It need not necessarily be directly related to scientific work but could be fund-raising, voluntary administrative help or, if you are lucky, relevant work experience. Passive membership will not really be considered as good evidence of either your commitment or your energy and enthusiasm to get the job done.

It is probably wise to state that your commitment to the environment does not mean you are against development or industry but you are for environmentally responsible development.

Communication skills

A lot of jobs in this sector benefit from the ability to communicate effectively. This can involve defending an idea, enforcing the law, advising the public, supervising a project, promoting and selling a proposal or persuading a committee. Make sure you can provide the evidence. It is an acquired skill for most people and one that many scientists, particularly environmental ones, ignore or think is unimportant. For those of you still at college or university, get involved in your societies and clubs and make an effort to communicate effectively.

Computing skills

Increasingly useful in almost all jobs, the ability to use a keyboard and some knowledge of database management, spreadsheets and word processing is essential and if you do not have these skills it is worth making the effort to acquire them.

Report writing skills

The ability to write coherently, concisely, accurately and to a deadline is always a useful skill. Good written reports or projects, such as PhD theses, dissertations or honours projects, are effective evidence of this skill. Also remember to keep copies of any publications you are involved with. Take your thesis with you to interview, particularly if it is well written and presented. Some job seekers prepare and present a report about some aspect of the prospective employer's company or organisation.

Vacation work or previous work experience

Most employers are attracted to applicants who have some work experience. This may be related to environmental problems such as voluntary work with the British Trust for Conservation Volunteers (BTCV) or with another conservation body. Short term contract work with conservation groups is invaluable experience. Active commercial experience (such as sales work or business management) in a non-environmental organisation can be extremely valuable and attractive, particularly to consultancies. The message is that any work experience which gives evidence of your abilities to do the job will be useful and should be mentioned.

Commercial sense

Many employers, particularly in the large consultancies complain of the difficulties of getting well qualified scientists with commercial ability and understanding of a balance sheet. Vacation work could be used to get these skills or, alternatively, a stint working in the commercial sector may prove helpful.

The above are probably amongst the most important factors looked for by most employers in the environmental sector. Organisational skills, social skills and a driving licence have not been mentioned but may be required by particular employers. Not everyone will have all the abilities mentioned but you should have a number of core skills on which to base your application. A good number of the factors are easily attainable by bright, committed individuals and if you are serious about jobs in the environment you will be well advised to acquire as many as possible. Many of you will have other skills, abilities and experiences which are not mentioned here. They should be included in any application as long as they are relevant and contribute evidence of your ability to do the job.

FINDING OUT ABOUT THE JOBS

Advertised vacancies

The *New Scientist* and *The Guardian* (particularly on Fridays) are generally considered to be the most useful publications and are well established sources of vacancy information. The other national newspapers also carry relevant vacancies, and professional journals are often sources of directly relevant vacancies. Local and regional newspapers are also worth keeping an eye on, particularly for short term and vacation opportunities and for specific regional vacancies.

Speculative applications

This form of application has become increasingly popular amongst job seekers in recent times. They are a useful means of application for good students who know what they want and have evidence in support. Vague open letters which only hint at evidence are not generally successful. This form of application is probably the most difficult to get right but is often treated quite casually by job seekers.

The good speculative application should consist of a comprehensive *curriculum vitae* (CV) accompanied by a covering letter of explanation. Even though the application is speculative it should still focus on the employer or company to which it is being sent. So the message here is that a great deal of research must be done before attempting speculative applications.

Employers vary as to how they respond to this type of approach. Most will react positively to good, targeted, well presented and coherent applications but will ignore the rest. Some employers actually use this method as an effective means of recruitment and rarely advertise any vacancies in the press. This is particularly true of smaller companies who have vacancies less often.

Whether you, the job seeker, should use this method or not depends on what you want and how much time you have. If you are prepared to spend the energy and effort researching a sensible 'hit list' which can be compiled from specialist directories (see Reference section) and then targeting each employer with a well thought-out application which attempts to match your skills and needs with those of the company, then it is a useful form of application. Otherwise it is often a depressing tunnel of rejection letters at best or, more frequently, nothing at all. A discussion with a careers adviser or course tutor is often useful before moving down this route.

Recruitment agencies

These can be useful to job seekers with specific requirements, such as those that don't have the resources to search the press for vacancies or who want a job in a specific region of the country. Many employers also use agencies, some just as a 'topping up' measure while others use them exclusively for all their recruitment needs.

In recent years a number of recruitment agencies have established themselves in the 'green' market. They will try and match your needs (for example, companies with no defence contracts or those which do not use live animal experimentation, or employers with a commitment to protecting the environment) with a suitable employer. For many job seekers, particularly the strongly committed, these agencies are a useful extra and can be extremely helpful. Job changers may find that an agency is the best way to move job, particularly if it involves a slight change of direction or information on a new set of employers. Another advantage is that if the agency is good it does take a lot of the grind out of the search for suitable vacancies, but check to see that the agency is reputable and has a good client list in the particular field you wish to pursue. A number of more prominent agencies are listed at the end of the book under 'references'.

However, as with speculative letters, don't expect miracles. You will still have to do your homework and the state of the economy will have a bearing on the success of the agency. The agency may be able to organise some interviews on your behalf but it will still be up to you to secure the job offer.

Peter Sills, the Director of one such recruitment agency, Oakleaf Recruitment, which specialises in placements in the environmental field says:

'Many small to medium sized environmental consultancies or com-panies just do not have the time or resources to recruit themselves. Rather than advertising a post and sorting through the applications, which may run into hundreds, it is often easier for them to pick up the 'phone and ask us to find them suitable candidates. Many vacancies are simply not advertised.

Once registered with Oakleaf, the candidates are kept informed of all vacancies in their declared area of interest and locality. A good recuitment consultant should be able to assess candidates' potential accurately, only presenting them to suitable employers, and in a thoroughly professional manner. At Oakleaf, for example, we stan-dardise CVs and send them to potential employers without the candidates' names or addresses in order to protect their interests. If necessary, we can also further explain to our clients the candidate's qualifications and experience in advance of the interview, thus giving the candidate every opportunity to impress the prospective employer at the interview. Consequently, the job seeker has nothing to lose – as the services are free and confidential – and a large advantage to gain.'

Most job seekers get jobs using one of the above methods. Of course, tutors, vacation work supervisors, work colleagues and friends are also valuable sources of vacancy information. It is probably best to use a combination of methods and with good application forms one of them will produce the offer.

APPLYING FOR A JOB

Application forms

What makes a good application form? This is a question frequently posed and rarely answered adequately. Most careers advisers would agree that a good application is one that matches the skills and requirements posed by the advertisement, or by an employer's brochure if it is a speculative one. So it follows that what may be a good application for one job may not necessarily be so for another. In environmental jobs this is particularly true and many applicants are often disappointed that the CV that got them the holiday job whilst they were at college does not do the trick after graduation.

Here are a few tips to good application forms:

Be specific about your qualifications and experience. This should include specific details on projects and essays if they are relevant. It is no use applying for a job in marine conservation, say, and omitting the project you did on estuarine pollution. However, be careful not to use up pages explaining some complex technique in minute detail. Think of the person reading the application: what do they need to know about you?

Mention voluntary and vacation work experience. Many people who apply for jobs in this sector feel embarrassed mentioning the job running the corner shop or the stint cleaning cucumbers, or 'plucking turkeys every Christmas for the last five years to make some money'. Most work experience, however menial, is usually relevant and often much more pertinent than you think. Running the corner shop, stock taking, ordering, pricing, and so on, is extremely valuable commercial experience. Many employers, particularly those with a commercial element to the business (such as environmental consultancies) would be interested in that kind of experience. It needs to be effectively presented to demonstrate your abilities and any new skills that you acquired during the work.

Be neat and tidy. This is particularly appropriate in any competitive job market and environmental work is one of the most competitive. There is also often an assumption that people who work in the environmental sector are less stringent about presentation. This is rarely the case. First class presentation is always a help to any application and is a good indication of your eagerness and firm intention.

Be prepared to 'market yourself'. It is no good referring obliquely to your skills or neglecting to mention work experience or good results. Because you have to compete with a lot of other very suitable people you will need to make your application stand out. A positive assertive approach is a help along that path.

Read the job description. This applies to all jobs. Make sure you give evidence of your ability to meet the requirements mentioned. It is no use ignoring the ones you do not meet or cannot do. Address the problem positively, mentioning ways to overcome the lack of experience or whatever it happens to be. If you ignore or fail to answer the requirements specified in the job description the selectors will probably fail to invite you to interview.

Be efficient. Basic common sense tells you to check your spelling, use good paper which is clean and uncreased (it can, of course, be recycled), and black ink or typescript. Posting applications in appropriately-sized envelopes using first class postage also improves the presentation of your 'product' and says a lot about you the candidate and your enthusiasm for the job.

Interviews

A good application form does not get you a job though it may get you an interview. But once you manage to get to this stage you are in with an excellent chance of getting the job. Most employers do not bother interviewing applicants who don't meet their basic requirements. Interviewing is a costly business in terms of time and money and most employers will try to ensure that they only shortlist candidates who appear, on paper, to fit their criteria for the job. So it is down to you to impress the interviewer and convince them of your ability.

In this part of the selection process employers in the environmental sector are no different from any other employers – they want the best candidate. And like any other part of the selection process, to be successful takes time and careful preparation.

The preparation for interview should cover your specific field of interest and you should ensure that you are as well-informed as possible about your prospective employer. This can sometimes be extremely difficult if the company is recently established or fairly small. However, if this is the case try phoning the company and having a chat on the phone or arranging a pre-interview visit. Most will not see this as being pushy but will value the interest you are expressing. Course tutors and careers services are often aware of small employers, particularly if they are local, and are a useful source of information.

Many employers in this sector will also expect you to have some knowledge of relevant current affairs. Reading the environmental sections of the national press and the *New Scientist* should help to keep you up-to-date. This is particularly important for jobs with pressure groups (such as Greenpeace or World Wide Fund For Nature), enforcement agencies (the National Rivers Authority, for example) and consultancies in general.

Many students when attempting interviews for the first time are often surprised that they are expected to defend their thesis or elaborate on a technique or the experimental design of the project. A lot of jobs in this area are extremely technical and may involve a clear understanding of the complex technical or legal data. Be prepared to discuss, and if required, to defend your point of view. The interviewers are not trying to trick you or to show how clever they are (although it may occasionally happen). It is a good way of finding out how much you really know and how well you cope with a stressful situation.

As with any job interview do make an attempt to show that it is important to you; dress appropriately. Many employers in this sector are particularly sensitive about the 'bearded wonder' jibe, i.e. anyone with a too blatant 'green' appearance or attitude, and will not take kindly to those who cultivate this image at interview.

There are a variety of sources of information about how safely to negotiate an interview. Your careers service, library and local Jobcentre should have a good selection. If you feel that interviews are your weak point then do make an effort to consult someone about it.

Rejections

Some of you may get to this point of the chapter and be quite indignant. You have done everything as you should, but you have yet to land that job. Most jobs in this area are fiercely competitive. Luck often has its part in who finally makes it over the last hurdle. You will be downhearted if, or when (it happens to everybody at some stage) that letter saying 'no' arrives. You then have to decide what it means to you.

If you are totally convinced that this is the career for you then you will have to keep going. Learn from each application you make. At what stage were you rejected? If you never get interviews it may mean your application forms are not up to standard in some way. Get a second opinion from a tutor, careers adviser or someone in that line of business. If you frequently get to interview stage but never quite get the job this often suggests that your method of application is good but some aspect of your interview technique is faulty and needs attention.

It is never easy to analyse your own faults or omissions. But it needs to be done if you are to get that job. Remember, you will probably get a few, or even lots of rejections but it only takes one job offer to solve the problem.

For details on environmental organisations, specialist recruitment agencies, courses and further information, please see the reference section at the back of the book.

6 GENERAL TRENDS IN ENVIRONMENTAL CAREERS

INTRODUCTION

The environment is an extremely broad employment sector and there is every sign that it will become still larger and more diverse.

- A 1990 research report by the consultancy ECOTEC forecast that the pollution control sector (including waste management) is likely to grow by 8.5 per cent per annum.

- The Centre for the Exploitation of Science and Technology has forecast a need for the UK to spend £140 billion (and for the EU to spend £850 billion) by the year 2000 on environmental equipment, products and services.

- The US Environmental Protection Agency has estimated that America already spends 2 per cent of its gross national product (GNP) on environmental protection and remediation – roughly US$100 billion per annum.

- At present, more than 100,000 persons in the UK and 1.5 million in the EC are directly employed in the environmental sector – and these numbers are likely to rise in the future.

Although career opportunities in the environmental sciences have been affected by the global economic recession of the early 1990s, they have not been as badly hit as other parts of the economy – perhaps because of the diversity and relative youth of the environmental sector.

One area where there has been a cut back in opportunities is education. Although environmental education is still a cross curricular theme in the national curriculum it does not have a high profile. Local education authorities have been strapped for cash and as a result many environmental education advisory and support services such as field study centres have been lost.

Environmental work still relies on the strength of other sectors of the economy. Therefore, future prospects for environmental scientists are always linked to those of the rest of the economy.

One important growth area in the last few years has been the use of environmental experts from European Union countries to help tackle environmental problems in eastern Europe, Russia and the former Soviet Socialist Republics. Experts in most demand are environmental managers for business and industry, advisers on environment and environmental education policies and practice and experts in the conservation of the natural and built environment. The British Council, many NGOs, educational institutions, businesses and consultancies in the UK have contracts for major schemes from the British government, the European Union and the World Bank.

Within the environmental sciences, different sectors have varying outlooks – some, better than others. The lack of long-term career opportunities for young environmental scientists entering research continues to cause concern. On the other hand, it is clear that local government, regulatory agencies, the environmental consultancies and industry are still recruiting environmental scientists with relevant experience.

Indeed, there are few areas of public service or industrial activity which have not been affected by the new environmental imperative. Professionals in all walks of life are learning environmental skills and environmental scientists are applying their training to areas of activity which were once considered as somehow separate from the environment.

The law, accountancy, planning, surveying, engineering and many other areas of work are now recognised as having an important environmental component. Indeed, the Americans have coined the term 'Green Collar Workers' to describe this new breed of environmental professional.

The key questions for the future of environmental careers are:

- How permanent is this development in the environmental professions?

- To what extent will environmental issues be incorporated into the work of other, more traditional, careers?

Although these questions cannot be answered with any degree of certainty, the environmental careers market is likely to continue expanding because it is driven by a unique combination of statutory regulation and personal commitment.

The problem for those seeking environmental employment is that they are presently receiving contradictory signals from the employment market. On the one hand, the recession has hit all areas of business activity and school leavers as well as environmental graduates with no career experience are finding difficulty in securing their first professional job. On the other hand, graduates with relevant career experience, second degrees, or specialist skills are managing to find appropriate employment in both the UK and the European market where experience is much in demand.

Perhaps of all the factors influencing the future it is that of Europe which will most affect the development of environmental careers. On 1 January 1993 the Single Market was put in place in Europe and as a result, new opportunities will continue to open up for environmental scientists. The European Commission has estimated that some 1.5 million people in the Union are already directly employed in the environmental sector – either in environmental management or pollution control. The Commission has forecast that this will grow to three million by the end of the decade – due in no small way to the increase in environmental legislation. Since 1967, there have been more than 300 EU environmental directives and regulations and the trend is towards still more environmental legislation to introduce measures like taxes on the price of such things as fuel, so that market forces will achieve the desired results. Where there is regulation, laws may become partly based on voluntary commitment.

Waste management and water treatment are two sectors which are expected to grow particularly rapidly as a result of EU legislation. These are both areas in which UK technical expertise is especially strong, which will undoubtedly affect sources of future employment. On the environmental monitoring side, EU legislation and its UK implementation will also mean more work in the fields of environmental assessment and auditing – both for practitioners working within industry and for external consultants.

TRENDS IN ENVIRONMENTAL EDUCATION, TRAINING AND INFORMATION

Education

The need to produce more and better trained environmental scientists is leading colleges and universities to offer a greater variety of environmental courses. For existing first degree courses, colleges are adjusting course content to produce more employable graduates by addressing the needs of employers more thoroughly in addition to developing more applied courses.

At a postgraduate level, masters courses in environmental management and technology are growing in number and gaining in popularity. In particular, the courses at Imperial College in Environmental Technology and at Manchester University in Environmental Pollution and Control have produced a steady stream of well qualified students.

Distance learning is also likely to become more popular and residential short courses, too, will become increasingly important for those already in work: the demand for continuing education for environmental professionals will go on expanding.

The other key trend is towards integrating environmental information into existing traditional disciplines such as the MBA (Environment) at Kent University, BSc in Civil and Environmental Engineering at University College, London and BSc Physics with Environmental Sciences at Sheffield Hallam University.

Training

Employment opportunities in the environmental sector appear likely to grow. This will require a sustained, quality programme of environmental training – rather than solely relying on training on-the-job which has too often been the only form of training available in many sectors of British industry.

Training is already becoming better established in certain environmental sectors. Most notably, there is the Council for Occupational Standards and Qualifications in Environmental Conservation (COSQUEC), the Waste Management Industry Training Board (WAMITAB) and Careers, Education and Training for Agriculture and the Countryside (CETAC). They have been established as lead bodies providing a framework of standards and qualifications to stimulate and help in training: COSQUEC dealing with conservation, WAMITAB with waste management and CETAC with agriculture and countryside.

If the environmental employment sector is to continue to develop in a healthy manner, there is a clear need for similar developments in environmental training, both for new recruits and those already working within it.

Training of professionals in the ecology and environmental management sector is relatively well developed. This compares with the industrial sector where it largely consists of expensive conferences and seminars rather than practical interactive training (though there are, of course, some exceptions). This situation will have to change in the future and may, therefore, become an employment growth area within the environmental sector itself.

Information

The information technology revolution, which has created a generation of information scientists, is now likely to revolutionise the field of environmental practice.

Many environmental activities such as ecological surveying, or environmental monitoring and analysis produce mountains of data: this is most easily handled using computers. Geographical data such as land use patterns or cartographic information is increasingly becoming digitised and this data is now often held and accessed through geographic information systems. More generally speaking, the whole business of accessing environmental information will become fundamental to the development of jobs within the environmental sector. This development of environmental information systems and software and the management of environmental data is therefore a clear growth area in the environmental careers market.

Environmental information is held by a variety of bodies including governmental agencies, publishers, and environmental consultancies. Governmental agencies exist at Harwell (land), Warren Springs (air) and Water Research Centre (water), which hold environmental information. They all employ specialists to research and handle data. Publications such as the newsletter *Environment Business* and its associated *Environment Business Magazine* and the *ENDS Report*, the Business and Environment Programme of the Environment Council and Croner's, deal in environmental information and their success reflects the need for high quality information on the environment. Certain environmental consultancies have become well known for handling environmental data – such as Aspinwall & Company Ltd. who provide data on waste management.

TRENDS IN ENVIRONMENTAL REGULATION

Legislative trends

The key driving force behind many recent environmental initiatives, in both the public and private sectors, has been the rapid development of environmental law. Much of this legislation originates from the EU and there are a number of clear examples of environmental legislation directly stimulating new skills and creating new career opportunities. The 1989 Water Act and the Environmental Protection Act in 1990 have both helped to stimulate the environmental employment market by introducing new regulatory regimes, and stricter requirements. At an EU level, directives and regulations both directly and indirectly create environmental employment. For instance, EU laws are helping to develop the relatively new professions of environmental auditing and assessment and this trend is expected to continue.

Regulatory agencies

The main environmental regulatory authorities in England and Wales are Her Majesty's Inspectorate of Pollution (HMIP), and the National Rivers Authority (NRA). There are also equivalent bodies in Scotland, i.e. Her Majesty's Industrial Pollution Inspectorate and the River Purification Boards, and in Northern Ireland, i.e. the Department of the Environment (Northern Ireland) and its Water Service. The Health and Safety Executive, although not primarily an environmental regulator, does an increasing amount of environmental work as well.

Although the situation has yet to be resolved, it appears that the HMIP and the NRA will be combined to form a single regulatory agency to be known as the 'Environment Agency'. These organisations will also be joined by the local authorities' waste regulatory services.

These regulatory authorities are an important source of employment for suitably qualified and experienced people. This is likely to continue to be the case, but only if governments are prepared to give these agencies adequate resources.

Local authorities

Local authorities presently have statutory responsibilities relating to waste regulation and disposal activities, mineral planning, development control, air pollution and noise control, countryside management and environmental health. The waste regulatory services are likely to become absorbed into the new Environment Agency. These responsibilities, and hence job opportunities, are increasing as new laws take effect and people become more concerned about the quality of their local environment. Indeed, with the increasing centralisation of governmental power, the environmental field is one of the few areas in which local government still exercises power and influence.

Many local authorities have produced environmental policy statements – setting out their commitment to the environment and their objectives for improving it. Some have audited the environmental performance of their services, others have produced reports on the state of the environment, and this is leading to new career opportunities for environmental scientists in local government.

Despite having expenditure tightly controlled, many local authorities have created new environmental positions. Most authorities now have recycling officers and some are appointing staff to undertake local Agenda 21 initiatives. It is now possible to pursue an environmental career in local government without becoming an environmental health officer. It is likely that local councils will become increasingly important employers of environmental scientists.

ENVIRONMENTAL BUSINESS OPPORTUNITIES

Industry

Large sectors of industry now see the employment of environmental professionals as a permanent addition to the workforce. In some cases this has simply meant additional responsibilities for the company's health and safety manager. More fundamentally, many sectors of industry are now conducting internal environmental site audits, managing their waste streams (in this context, 'streams' means the origin, handling and disposal methods) and energy usage, setting up environmental management systems and producing environmental reports. All these activities have meant opportunities for environmental scientists and this is likely to be a continuing trend. Where the expertise is not available within the company, external environmental consultants are often used.

Consultancy

Demand for environmental consultancy services has grown considerably over the past decade. This is clearly demonstrated by the rapid rise in the number of companies providing consultancy services. Most of these consultancies concentrate on either ecological or industrial practice, while the larger companies offer a comprehensive range of services.

During the 1980s environmental consultancies tended to grow in size (partly through mergers and buy-outs), but the recent and likely future trend is towards a larger number of smaller, more specialised consultancies.

Clearly, there is a limit to the number of consultancies which can survive in the market. However, the size of this market still appears to be growing (especially given the development of a wider European market) with relatively new areas such as environmental marketing, product life-cycle analysis, and environmental auditing, all creating demand for consultants.

Consultancy appears to be an attractive option for many graduates due to the variety of work experience offered. However, competition for positions is strong and people with second degrees and experience are usually the preferred candidates.

The future is likely to see an expansion of the consultancy market and this will not be solely confined to environmental consultancies. Engineering and management consultancies have recently been developing their environmental services which means that graduates with management or engineering skills may also find employment in the consultancy field.

It has always been rather paradoxical that environmental consultants should advise on environmental regulation and management while being largely unregulated themselves. As a new profession this is, perhaps, inevitable but these consultancies are now becoming more professional by encouraging their staff to join professional institutions (such as the Institution of Environmental Sciences) and are themselves forming professional associations or organisations – such as the Association of Environmental Consultancies and the Institute of Environmental Assessment. Indeed, the first EU-wide move, to regulate the market are shortly expected with the registration of Accredited Environmental Verifiers under the EU's Eco-audit Regulation. The Department of Trade and Industry is also developing a register of recommended environmental consultants which businesses can use. Clearly, in order to practise as a consultant in the future it will become increasingly important to have some form of officially recognised, professional status.

Environmental technology

Environmental technology will continue to play an important part both in shaping the content of college courses and in the provision of employment opportunities.

In the 1960s and 1970s, developments tended to focus on controlling the amount and toxicity of pollutants discharged from factories through so-called 'end of pipe' technologies. The 1980s and 1990s have seen a more fundamental shift towards the development of 'clean technologies' which produce less pollution – indeed the best technologies or techniques used are now often required by law.

The need for process plant to meet tighter emission specifications will stimulate the research and development market and the manufacture of new, cleaner plants. This will, in turn, also provide career opportunities for environmental engineers and technologists.

Both the new, clean production technologies and those more recently installed (or 'retro-fitted') into older plants will require extensive monitoring programmes to ensure that performance and emission specifications are met. This will, in turn, provide continuing employment for environmental scientists.

Green consumerism and the retail sector

It is difficult not to overstate the importance of environmental issues to the future of the distributive trades. Led by progressive retailers such as the Body Shop, and do-it-yourself chains like B&Q, shops are now paying increasing attention to their suppliers' activities, to how their customers use and dispose of their products, and to environmental reporting.

This attention to the 'greenness' of goods and commodities is partly a result of consumer pressure and partly foresight by the companies in question – focusing on the market share of 'green goods' and the impact of new legislation on goods and packaging (with the EU's Eco-labelling regulation and its proposed packaging directive).

These actions mean that there are now opportunities in the retail and wholesale sectors for environmental graduates and others with human resource and marketing skills. This is likely to be a key growth area of future employment as few products have no environmental implications and many have serious effects.

Conservation, and environment and development

In the UK, the area of land protected by special environmental designations continues to grow. Sites of Special Scientific Interest, National Parks, and Areas of Outstanding Natural Beauty and their equivalents, require varying amounts of countryside management skills. While not being especially financially rewarding (indeed many projects are purely voluntary), conservation work is labour intensive and continues to provide employment for a significant proportion of the environmental workforce. As areas of land with unique amenities or special protection increase, so do the various pressures on this land. It is therefore most likely that countryside management will continue as a major source of employment for ecologists and environmental scientists.

The United Nations' Conference on Environment and Development (UNCED) held in Rio de Janeiro in 1992 made it clear that even though nations do not necessarily share the same goals, environmental protection and sustainable development are firmly on the international agenda. Very much connected to this is the question of the debt crisis in the 'third world' which has many direct effects on the global environment, much discussed in public debate over recent years. Issues such as pollution, energy usage and the depletion of resources are central to trade and development, and whether it is sustainable in future. The environment, and development in general, have therefore become central issues to international cooperation and have featured prominently in the work of the World Bank, national banks, governmental and international development agencies, and charities. These activities have generated opportunities for environmental scientists working on everything from village-scale water supply projects to major infrastructure works for example, dams, airports, power stations, and it looks as if this will continue for the foreseeable future.

THE MEDIA

The growth of interest in the environment is linked to the increased coverage of environmental topics and issues in newspapers and magazines and on television and radio. People with a broad understanding of the environment are ideal for advising on and writing materials and programmes designed for general public consumption. Although a celebrity may be the one publicised with the project, researchers and authors are needed to provide essential support. Of course, there is nothing to stop anyone with an interest in and knowledge of the environment writing speculative articles for local papers. Very many are successful, especially if the writer can guarantee to provide a regular column.

The Government's programme 'going for Green' is designed to help the public know how to do their bit for the environment. If successful, it will be producing a range of materials.

SUMMARY

The environment is a broad and youthful employment sector which is set to become still larger and more diverse. It has not been as badly affected by the global recession as some other employment sectors and there are opportunities – especially for those with relevant qualifications and experience.

Environmental scientists and managers are now recognised as members of a new profession and the term 'Green Collar Workers' has been used to describe them. The environmental professions are developing rapidly but there is still a need for better trained environmental scientists.

Large sections of industry and the service sector now see the employment of environmental professionals as a permanent and valuable addition to the workforce. The future is likely to see an expansion of the consultancy market to service these sectors where there is insufficient in-house expertise.

The demand for both the new, clean production technologies and the older 'retro-fitted' ones will provide opportunities in the environmental technology sector as well as require extensive environmental monitoring programmes. This will, in turn, provide continuing employment for environmental scientists and technologists.

Environmental factors are of vital importance to the future of the distributive trades. Consequently, the retail sector will be a key growth area for future environmental employment opportunities for people with the right skills.

Countryside management will continue to be a steady source of employment for ecologists and environmental scientists. International environment and development projects should also generate more opportunities for environmental scientists working on appropriate technology projects or major infrastructure works – but careers in this area are challenging and usually dependent on continued funding from governments and international aid agencies.

APPENDIX I

ENVIRONMENTAL SALARIES AND BENEFIT REVIEW –
December 1994

Introduction

Environment Business published its third survey of environmental salaries and benefits in early 1995. It noted that specialist environmental recruitment agencies are busy again. People are changing jobs and while this seems to be a positive indicator for the whole environmental service sector, no one has yet claimed that there is a permanent upturn in demand for qualified staff.

The survey is based on replies from 537 people working in 480 organisations. The information was collected in December 1994 and January 1995. The survey excludes consultants working abroad.

An overview

Salaries for all job functions covered in the survey tend to increase with experience and age but there is a noticeable jump for staff between three and five years after postgraduate qualification.

Smaller consultancies generally pay 8–12% lower rates than

average. The best paid are those with top jobs in large companies. In middle size industries the highest earnings are in the pharmaceutical and petrochemical industries. For senior jobs in consultancies, post graduate qualifications are becoming a necessity.

Many salaries had not been increased over the previous 12 months. Nevertheless, expectations of increases lay between 3.5 and 5.1% over the next year.

Job functions and titles

Respondents select from pre-described job function categories and give the job title they use. The survey confirmed that titles for similar positions vary widely from company to company, so the following generic titles have been used to indicate the function specified:

Industry

Group Director: Director or senior manager, responsible at group level for company-wide environmental policy development and implementation.
Plant Manager: Manager or Director, responsible for environmental management at an individual plant or site, eg Health, Safety and Environment Manager; Operations Manager; Quality and Environmental Manager.
Site Engineer: Engineer or equivalent, responsible for a variety of specific site or plant environmental tasks, eg Environmental Systems Coordinator; Senior Process Engineer.
Specialist: Individual with particular skills, eg Environmental Technician; Ecologist; Environmental Chemist.

Consultancy

Partner: Director or equivalent with a central role in the running of the consultancy.

Senior Consultant: A senior consultant developing business for the consultancy as well as managing major projects.

Project Manager: Consultant responsible for smaller projects usually with the help of a small team.

Field Operative: Typically an Auditor, Assessor or Surveyor undertaking field work for the consultancy.

Specialist: An individual whose particular skills are being employed in a specialist capacity, eg Hydrologist, Chemist, Ecologist.

Environmental technology and contracting companies

Director: Board director or equivalent with a central role in running the organisation.

Middle Manager: With project responsibilities, eg Development Manager; Technical Director; Quality Manager.

Field Engineer/Specialist: Typically Air Pollution Engineers; Systems Engineers; Environmental Scientists.

Regulators: Local authority and other enforcement agency personnel.

CURRENT AVERAGE SALARIES

Industry

Group managers	£35,300
Plant managers	£26,100
Site engineers	£16,600
Specialists	£17,400

Consultancies

Partners	£41,200
Senior consultants	£30,100
Project managers	£23,900
Field operatives	£17,700
Specialists	£17,300

Technology/contractors

Directors	£39,000

Middle managers	£29,000
Specialists	£18,300
Regulators	£21,700

Other benefits

These include cars, contribution to pension scheme (usually between six and seven per cent of salary), private medical insurance and bonus/profit sharing.

APPENDIX II COURSES

UNDERGRADUATE COURSES

ABERDEEN UNIVERSITY
Environmental Science; (Ecology); (Physical Sciences)
BSc 3/4 Years Full-time

ASKHAM BRYAN COLLEGE
Environmental Management (Engineering)
Diploma Of Higher Education (Subject to validation by the University of Leeds)
2 Years Full-time

ENTRANCE QUALIFICATIONS A levels/Scottish Highers required: A levels in maths and a science or 4 Scottish Higher grades required: Cs. **Other entry qualifications:** GNVQ (Advanced) engineering or science at Merit grade, BTEC ND at Merit level (range of subjects). Mature applicants: Welcome but must satisfy the University's general entry requirements, eg Access course & other. **STUDENT NUMBERS Annual applications:** New course. **COURSE PROFILE:** Engineering is the core of this course and is linked to the land based industries including forestry, horticulture, agriculture, waste management and environmental control. It has components of management skills, environmental studies, maths and computing. Options are available.

ASKHAM BRYAN COLLEGE
Land Management and Technology
BSc 1 Year Full-time

ENTRANCE QUALIFICATIONS Selection criteria: HND Merit level or Dip HE. **Mature applicants:** Applications welcome with equivalent qualifications. **STUDENT NUMBERS Annual applications:** 40 (1994) **Annual places:** 20–25. **EMPLOYMENT ENTERED:** Local authorities, garden centre managers, private landscapers, NRA, countryside rangers. **COURSE PROFILE:** The technological base of the HND changes to a more academic approach to business management and options including: conservation, land restoration, landscape architecture, agricultural production systems, public relations and management of practical economics. Also includes an 'investigation project'. **FUTURE DEVELOPMENTS:** Course currently being modified in order to be considered for upgrading to honours degree level.

ASKHAM BRYAN COLLEGE
Landscape Management
BSc (Hons) Full-time (Subject to validation by the University of Leeds)

ENTRANCE QUALIFICATIONS GCSEs/SCEs required: Maths and English. GCSEs/SCEs preferred: Biology, chemistry, geography, history, art. A levels/Scottish Highers required/preferred: 2 A-levels/Scottish Highers from geography, biology, business studies, economics, chemistry. Grade: Scottish Higher C. **Other entry qualifications:** BTEC ND at Merit level, GNVQ (Advanced) at Merit grade & additional units or A/AS subjects, other qualifications on individual consideration. Mature applicants: Welcome, must show evidence of ability to study at degree level (eg Access) **STUDENT NUMBERS Annual applications:** New course. **COURSE PROFILE:** The course aims to develop an application and understanding of the social, economic and institutional context of landscape management. Developed in consultation with the industry, it includes: law, policy, finance, history, plant use, science and management skills, including contact management.

UNIVERSITY OF BATH
Biology & Applied Biology
BSc 3 Years Full-time 4 Years Sandwich

ENTRANCE QUALIFICATIONS GCSEs/SCEs required: English, maths and one science. A-levels/Scottish Highers required: Biology. A level/ Scottish Higher preferred: Chemistry. Grade: Scottish Higher B. **Other entry qualifications:** AS levels accepted as half an A level, International

UNIVERSITY OF LONDON
WYE COLLEGE

SERVICE TO THE RURAL COMMUNITY WORLD-WIDE.

Well established undergraduate and postgraduate degree programmes at the University of London's rural campus and its centre for advanced teaching and research in the environment.

Undergraduate programmes (BSc)

Rural Environment Studies	Agriculture and the Environment
Countryside Management	Environmental Science

Postgraduate programmes (MSc)

Rural Resources and Environmental Policy	Sustainable Agriculture
Landscape Ecology, Design and Management	Applied Environmental Science

For further information contact: Academic Registrar (ref. ECH1), Wye College University of London, Ashford, Kent TN25 5AH, UK. Phone + 44 (0)1233 812401; Fax + 44 (0)1233 813320.

School of Arts and Sciences
Pathways on the BA/BSc(Hons) Modular Degree Programme

Biology*
Modules focus on behavioural, ecological and evolutionary biology.

Conservation Biology
(Single subject degree). Vocationally orientated towards wildlife and habitat conservation and management.

Environmental Studies*
Modules available for students from humanities or science backgrounds. Students may wish to specialise in one or more of three themes: Green Issues, Pollution Monitoring and Control, Biological Conservation.

*Minor and joint modes available now. Major and Single Honours modes available from September 1995, subject to validation.

Duration – Three years full-time, five years part-time.

Entry Requirements – Standard 'A' level entry: 10 points. BTEC National Diploma. Mature student entry: Encouraged to apply and considered on merit.

Further details from Dr. R. Howell, School of Arts and Sciences on ext 3646.

Deane Road, Bolton, Lancs., BL3 5AB. Tel. 01204 528851. Fax 01204 399074

BOLTON
INSTITUTE

Establishing a new University

Baccalaureate (28 points), BTEC Distinction and Merits. Mature applicants: Considered on individual merits but evidence of recent successful study essential. **STUDENT NUMBERS Annual applications:** c. 800 (1994). **Annual places:** 90 (1994). **EMPLOYMENT ENTERED:** Nature conservancy, Institute of Terrestrial Ecology, water companies, MoD conservation, ecology research, British Antarctic Survey. **COURSE PROFILE:** A broadly based biology course, with course modules (second and final year) in: ecology, evolution and environmental aspects. Sandwich options (for 12 months after the second year) enable students to work with potential employers.

BATH COLLEGE OF HIGHER EDUCATION
Environmental Science
BSc 3 Years Full-time

ENTRANCE QUALIFICATIONS GCSEs/SCEs required: Biology and geography. GCSEs/SCEs preferred: Any of chemistry, physics, maths English or double science. A levels/Scottish Highers preferred: Biology, chemistry, physics, geography. Grade: C or above. Mature applicants: Welcomed. **STUDENT NUMBERS Annual places:** 20 (1994). **EMPLOYMENT ENTERED:** NRA, water companies, RSPB, environmental departments of local authorities, teaching, MAFF, national parks. **COURSE PROFILE:** Year 1 consists of biology, geography and one subsidiary subject. Years 2 and 3 provide a balanced choice of modules from the two main subjects. Industrial placements available.

BATH COLLEGE OF HIGHER EDUCATION
Environmental Biology: Single Hons/Major Joint Hons/Minor
BSc 3 Years Full-time or CATS

ENTRANCE QUALIFICATIONS GCSEs/SCEs required: Biology. GCSEs/SCEs preferred: Chemistry, physics, double award science, maths and English. A levels/Scottish Highers preferred: Biology, chemistry, physics or environmental science. Grade: C or above. **Mature applicants:** Welcomed. **STUDENT NUMBERS Annual places:** 70 (1994). **EMPLOYMENT ENTERED:** NRA, water companies, RSPB, environmental departments of local authorities, teaching, MAFF, national parks, environmental consultancy. **COURSE PROFILE:** Year 1 consists of biology and two other subjects. Advanced years provide a choice of modules which include: ecology, adaptive physiology, historical ecology, biogeography, pollution, conservation, marine biology, disease and environment, remote sensing, health and environment and dissertation. Work placements are available.

BSc (Hons) Environmental Biology

which examines the relationship between humans, other living organisms and the natural environment. Modules include a choice from Scientific Foundation, Biological Distribution, Ecology, Adaptive Physiology, Biogeography, Historical Ecology, Community Ecology, Plant and Animal Production, Biological Impact of Pollution, Marine Biology, Disease and Environment, and a dissertation.

BSc (Hons) Environmental Science

which explores the environment from both a geographical and biological perspective. In addition to the biological component, modules include a choice from Global Environmental Issues, Rural Land-Use and Living Space, Management of Fluvial Systems, Management of Coastal Systems, Environmental Remote Sensing, Politics, Space and Environment, Landscape Heritage, Quarternary Science and Energy, and a dissertation.

For further information contact:
The Senior Registrar
Bath College of Higher Education
Newton Park, Bath BA2 9BN
☎ (01225) 873701

THE QUEEN'S UNIVERSITY OF BELFAST
Environmental Planning
BSc 3 Years + 1 Postgraduate Diploma Year for Graduates with 2.2 or better
Full-time

ENTRANCE QUALIFICATIONS GCSEs/SCEs required: Maths, English and art. GCSEs/SCEs preferred: Geography, biology. A levels/Scottish Highers required: 2 A levels/Scottish Highers including a mathematical subject (maths, physics) a social science subject (geography, Sociology, economics), art. **Mature applicants:** Encouragement given to mature students, especially those with BTEC, HND etc. **STUDENT NUMBERS Annual applications:** 195 (1994). **Annual places:** 22 (1994). **EMPLOYMENT ENTERED:** Town and country planning, tourism, housing, Rural Development Council. **COURSE PROFILE:** The course provides a broadly based introduction to the planning of the built environment, with the majority of graduates progressing to a postgraduate diploma course in Town & Country Planning to gain professional qualification. **FUTURE DEVELOPMENTS: A** new lecture course on Management; more emphasis to places on seeking short work placements with organisations.

THE QUEEN'S UNIVERSITY OF BELFAST
Environmental Biology
BSc (Hons) 3 Years (4 with 'Level O' intermediate year) Full-time

ENTRANCE QUALIFICATIONS GCSEs/SCEs required: Maths, English and biology. A levels/Scottish Highers required: 3 A levels/Scottish Highers to include biology and chemistry. A levels/Scottish Highers preferred: Any other science. Grade: C or above. **Mature applicants:** Welcome through appropriate Access Courses. **STUDENT NUMBERS Annual applications:** 160 (1994). **Annual places:** not available. **EMPLOYMENT ENTERED:** General, departments of Agriculture and Environment, further environmental science courses, education and computer applications. **COURSE PROFILE:** The first year constitutes a broad introduction to the biological sciences. The remaining two years focus on environmental biology, with an emphasis on organisms in their natural environments. Particular consideration is paid to the marine environment and genetic variation in natural populations. **FUTURE DEVELOPMENTS:** The course is currently under re-evaluation with other degree programmes in the School of Biology and Biochemistry.

THE QUEEN'S UNIVERSITY OF BELFAST
Environmental Chemistry
BSc (Hons) 3 Years Full-time

ENTRANCE QUALIFICATIONS GCSEs/SCEs required: English, maths and chemistry. GCSE/SCE preferred: Biology. A levels/Scottish Highers required: Chemistry. A levels/Scottish Highers preferred: Maths, biology. **Other entry qualifications:** International Baccalaureate (approx. 27 points), OND, AS, GNVQ acceptable as ancillaries with A level chemistry. Mature applicants: Must show evidence of recent academic attainment. **STUDENT NUMBERS Annual applications:** 90 (1994). **EMPLOYMENT ENTERED:** New course. **COURSE PROFILE:** Two years in common with the BSc (Hons) Chemistry degree. Final Year: chemistry of the earth, ocean and atmosphere; clean technologies and options from all branches of chemistry. Project on an environmental topic. Industrial placements available.

THE UNIVERSITY OF BIRMINGHAM
Applied And Environmental Geology
BSc 3 Years Full-time

ENTRANCE QUALIFICATIONS GCSEs/SCEs required: Maths and English grade C or above. GCSEs/SCEs preferred: Dual science award or individual science subjects. A levels/Scottish Highers required: Equivalent of 3 A levels from A levels/AS levels/Scottish Highers of which at least half must normally be in science subjects. A levels/Scottish Highers preferred: Sciences, maths, geography (English for Scottish Highers). Grade: Scottish Highers grade B. **Other entry qualifications:** BTEC, International/ European Baccalaureate. Mature applicants: Welcome with appropriate qualifications eg Open University credits or Access Course (science). **STUDENT NUMBERS Annual applications:** 86 (1994). **Annual places:** 20 (1994). **EMPLOYMENT ENTERED:** Major construction firms, hydrology (water authorities, river authorities), United Nations and overseas governments, consultancy (pollution control, waste disposal, environmental planning and management), DoE. **COURSE PROFILE:** First year provides a basic grounding in geology. Students then follow environmental and applied aspects of geology. Topics include natural and man-made hazards, environmental geo-chemistry, hydro-geology and engineering geology. Final year students have a choice of modules and select project work.

THE UNIVERSITY OF BIRMINGHAM
Environmental Biology
BSc 3 Years Full-time

ENTRANCE QUALIFICATIONS GCSEs/SCEs required: Biology, chemistry or double integrated science, maths and English at grade C or above. A levels/Scottish Highers required: 3 A levels including biology and at least one from chemistry, physics or maths or three A levels including chemistry and either physics or maths and one other subject or equivalent mixture of A/AS levels. Grade: Scottish Highers grade B. **Other entry qualifications:** BTEC, International/European Baccalaureate, Access Courses also considered. Mature applicants: Welcome. **STUDENT NUMBERS Annual applications:** 103 (1994). **Annual places:** 10 (1994). **EMPLOYMENT ENTERED:** DoE, MAFF, NRA, conservation bodies. **COURSE PROFILE:** A modular course structure gives considerable flexibility. A foundation course in the first year provides a broad and balanced view of contemporary biology and allows specialisation in the second and third years, with the opportunity to carry out an original research project.

THE UNIVERSITY OF BIRMINGHAM
Environmental Chemistry
BSc 3 Years Full-time

ENTRANCE QUALIFICATIONS GCSEs/SCEs required: Maths and English grade C or above. A levels/Scottish Highers required: Chemistry at A level or AS level. If chemistry is offered at AS level, maths must also be offered at A or AS level. If chemistry is offered at A level maths should preferably be offered at A or AS level. Grade: Scottish Higher grades open to individual negotiation. **Other entry qualifications:** Baccalaureates, HND etc. Access by agreement and individual negotiation. **Mature applicants:** Encouraged with realistic conditions offered. **STUDENT NUMBERS Annual applications:** 101 **EMPLOYMENT ENTERED:** New course. **COURSE PROFILE:** This is principally a chemistry course with a leaning towards environmental studies. Students will opt for the environmental modules in the second and third years. The students may also choose a third year research project with an environmental theme.

THE UNIVERSITY OF BIRMINGHAM
Civil Engineering With Environmental Management
BEng (Hons) 3 Years Full-time (Additional industrial placement year possible)

ENTRANCE QUALIFICATIONS GCSEs/SCEs required: Maths, English and a science and three others at grade C or above. GCSEs/SCEs preferred: A good variety of subjects. A levels/Scottish Highers required: Maths. A levels/Scottish Highers preferred: 2 other A levels/Scottish Highers chosen from physics, chemistry, geography, economics. Grade: Individually assessed. **Other entry qualifications:** HND, ND, International Baccalaureates and others welcomed. **Mature students:** Welcome but evidence of mathematical ability is essential. **STUDENT NUMBERS Annual applications:** 900 (1994). **Annual places:** 90 (1994). **EMPLOYMENT ENTERED:** Consultant civil engineers, environmental engineers, water industry eg NRA and water companies, and business. **COURSE PROFILE:** An accredited civil engineering degree with options to specialise in environmental subjects from the second year. A modular final year includes options in: water pollution, hazardous wastes, pollutant dispersal, political impacts and a significant piece of environmental project work. Industrial placements are available.

THE UNIVERSITY OF BIRMINGHAM
Environmental Science
BSc 3 Years Full-time

ENTRANCE QUALIFICATIONS: GCSEs/SCEs required: Maths and English grade C or above. A levels/Scottish Highers required: Equivalent of 3 A levels from A levels/Scottish Highers/AS levels including two A levels/Scottish Highers in science subjects or when a mixture of A/AS levels is offered at least three must be in science subjects (geography is considered a science subject). **Other entry qualifications:** BTEC, International/European Baccalaureate, Access Courses also considered. **STUDENT NUMBERS Annual places:** 40 (1995). **EMPLOYMENT ENTERED:** New course. **COURSE PROFILE:** Course builds on basic scientific principles to develop an understanding of real-world problems and issues. Physical, chemical and biological sciences are integrated in order to study long-term environmental change, medium term ecosystem changes and short-term process dynamics.

THE UNIVERSITY OF BIRMINGHAM
Chemical Engineering with Environmental Management
MEng 4 years Full-time

ENTRANCE QUALIFICATIONS GCSEs/SCEs required: Maths, sciences and English. A levels/Scottish Highers required: Maths and chemistry. A levels/Scottish Highers preferred: Physics and/or biology. Grade: Scottish Higher grade B or above. **Other entrance qualifications:** All applicants considered on their individual merits. **STUDENT NUMBERS Annual applications:** 20 (1994). **Annual places:** 20 (1994). **EMPLOYMENT ENTERED:** Chemical, food and water industries **COURSE PROFILE:** The course has a Chemical Engineering core with applications to Environmental Management. The environmental studies are concerned with the control of industrial emissions to the atmosphere, water and land.

BOLTON INSTITUTE OF HIGHER EDUCATION
1) Environmental Studies, 2) Conservation Biology
1) BSc/BA, 2) BSc 3 Years Full-time, 5 Years Part-time

ENTRANCE QUALIFICATIONS GCSEs/SCEs required: Science subject. GCSEs/SCEs preferred: Dual award science. A levels/Scottish Highers required: One in a science, geography or maths. **Mature applicants:** Treated on merit and all will be interviewed. **STUDENT NUMBERS Annual applications:** 210 (1994). **Annual places:** 25 (1994). **EMPLOYMENT ENTERED:** New courses. **COURSE PROFILE:** Environmental Studies – students may if they wish specialise in pollution monitoring and control or in natural history and habitat conservation. Other modules available on 'environmental issues' may be taken by arts-based students. Conservation Biology – vocationally orientated towards wildlife and habitat conservation and management. **FUTURE DEVELOPMENTS:** Countryside Management to be included in the course.

BOLTON INSTITUTE OF HIGHER EDUCATION
Environmental and Geotechnical Studies
BSc (Hons) 3 Years Full-time 4 Years Sandwich

ENTRANCE QUALIFICATIONS GCSEs/SCEs required: English, maths, science. A levels/Scottish Highers required: 2/3 from maths, geology, environmental studies, environmental science, chemistry, biology, geography.

Grade: Scottish Higher grades CCB or BB. **Other entry qualifications:** BTEC, HND/C environmental science, environmental studies, building construction, civil engineering, GNVQ (Merit at advanced level) science or the built environment. **Mature applicants:** Welcomed and considered on individual basis. **STUDENT NUMBERS Annual applications:** 5 (1995). **Annual places:** 15 (1995). **EMPLOYMENT ENTERED:** Environmental consultancy, waste disposal authorities, water companies, local authorities, NRA, conservation companies. **COURSE PROFILE:** Through an understanding of soils, rocks, water and ground-water, the course provides theoretical and practical skills for water treatment, reclamation of contaminated land and alleviation of pollution through the assessment of treatment options and the design of on-site works. **FUTURE DEVELOPMENTS:** From 1996 the course will be offered in part-time mode.

BOURNEMOUTH UNIVERSITY
Environmental Protection
BSc 3 or 4 Years (depending on qualifications) Full-time, 6 Years Part-time

ENTRANCE QUALIFICATIONS GCSEs/SCEs required: Maths, English and either chemistry or biology. GCSEs/SCEs preferred: Additional sciences. A levels/Scottish Highers preferred: 3 A levels including 2 sciences or 5 Scottish Highers including 3 at higher grade. **Other entry qualifications:** Combination of other qualifications and relevant experience may be appropriate. **Mature applicants:** Welcomed. A 4 year extended programme is run for people with a limited background in science. **STUDENT NUMBERS Annual applications:** 400 (1994). **Annual places:** 62 (1994) for 3 year programme. **EMPLOYMENT ENTERED:** New course. **COURSE PROFILE:** The degree stresses the importance of a multi-disciplinary approach to environmental protection and so includes scientific, legal and management components. Placements at the end of the first and second years provide students with the opportunity to work within an environmental organisation.

BOURNEMOUTH UNIVERSITY
Conservation Sciences
BSc (Hons) 3 or 4 Years (extended programme) Full-time

ENTRANCE QUALIFICATIONS GCSEs/SCEs required: Maths and English. GCSEs/SCEs preferred: Chemistry, physics, biology, geology, geography, environmental studies/science. A levels/Scottish Highers required: At least one from chemistry, physics, biology, geology, geography, environmental studies/science. Two preferred. Grade: Scottish Highers grade C or higher. **Mature applicants:** With relevant experience and demonstrated ability to work to degree level welcomed. **STUDENT NUMBERS Annual applications:** 250+ (1994). **Annual places:** 60 (1994). **EMPLOYMENT ENTERED:** New course. **COURSE PROFILE:** Broad based multi-disciplinary programme with range of options available in final year allowing specialisation towards personal preferences. Entry is possible on an extended (4 year) programme which provides an additional foundation year for students lacking the necessary science qualifications. Industrial placements available.

UNIVERSITY OF BRADFORD
Environmental Management And Technology
BSc 3 Years (or 4 Years thick sandwich) Full-time

ENTRANCE QUALIFICATIONS GCSEs/SCEs required: Maths. GCSEs/ SCEs preferred: At least one science subject. A levels/Scottish Highers required: any science A level eg Maths, physics, chemistry, biology or environmental science. **Other entry requirements:** AS levels counted as half an A level, other qualifications looked at on an individual basis, OND GVNQ International Baccalaureate all acceptable. **Mature applicants:** usually via Access into higher education. **STUDENT NUMBERS Annual applications:** 90+. **Annual places:** 30 (1994). **EMPLOYMENT ENTERED:** Water authorities, river authorities and consultancies. **COURSE PROFILE:** The course strikes a balance between environmental sciences, technology and management to enable students to become effective environmental managers.

UNIVERSITY OF BRADFORD
Environmental Science and Environmental Science & Geography
BSc 3 Years (or 4 Years sandwich) Full-time

ENTRANCE QUALIFICATIONS GCSEs/SCEs required: English and Maths grade C or above. GSCEs/SCEs preferred: Biology, chemistry, geography. A levels/Scottish Highers required: One science subject. A levels/Scottish Highers preferred: Biology, chemistry, geography, economics, maths, environmental science or physics. Scottish Higher Grades: CCC, BB and CCCC. **Other entrance qualifications:** Baccalaureate, HNC and Access courses. **Mature applicants:** Require evidence of recent academic performance at A level or equivalent standard. **STUDENT NUMBERS Annual applications:** 650 (1994). **Annual places:** 81 (1994). **EMPLOYMENT ENTERED:** Pollution control, environmental management, environmental health officers eg Bradford Council, planning officers eg North Yorkshire CC, river protection officers eg Yorkshire Water Authority, environmental consultancy, park rangers eg Epping Forest Field

Ranger. **COURSE PROFILE:** The course deals with the interaction between physical, biological, economic and social environments, with a particular focus on environmental management and planning. A third year of practical training provides work experience. **FUTURE DEVELOPMENTS:** Modularisation introduced 1994 has enabled a wider range of options to be introduced, this range is being extended to include further physical geography options.

UNIVERSITY OF BRIGHTON
Environmental Sciences
BSc 3 Years Full-time, 4 Year Sandwich

ENTRANCE QUALIFICATIONS GCSEs/SCEs required: English, maths. GCSEs/SCEs preferred: Laboratory based science subjects preferred. A levels/Scottish Highers preferred: A biological science, environmental science and geography preferred. Grade: D's or equivalent. **Other entry qualifications:** Qualifications equivalent to A levels are acceptable. **Mature applicants:** Welcomed and treated on their own merits. **STUDENT NUMBERS Annual applications:** 490 (1994). **Annual places:** 55 (1994). **EMPLOYMENT ENTERED:** Nature conservation, environmental planning, environmental impact assessment, environmental officers, water resource management, soil survey. **COURSE PROFILE:** Multi-disciplinary modular course, allowing specialisation after first year. Major themes include ecology and environmental management, the human and physical environments, energy management and conservation and environmental pollution.

UNIVERSITY OF THE WEST OF ENGLAND (BRISTOL)
Environmental Science
BSc (Hons) 3 Years with optional sandwich Full and Part-time

ENTRANCE QUALIFICATIONS GCSEs/SCEs required: Maths and English at grade C or above. A levels/Scottish Highers required: Two, one must be a science subject. **Other entry qualifications:** HND/HNC and others considered on merit. Possible entry into second stage. **Mature applicants:** Welcomed and considered on their own merit. **STUDENT NUMBERS Annual applications:** 500 (1994). **Annual places:** 80 (1994). **EMPLOYMENT ENTERED:** Not available. **COURSE PROFILE:** The course aims to produce practitioners of environmental science who have a broad understanding of the social, political and economic context within which environmental decisions are made. Year 1 provides a foundation for later stages. Options are introduced in year two. Final year options include environmental biotechnology, ecological survey, pollution control, environmental monitoring and analysis, language modules and science journalism. Students will undertake a research project in their final year. Industrial placements are available for sandwich students.

THE UNIVERSITY OF BUCKINGHAM
Law, Biology and the Environment
LLB 2 Years Full-time

ENTRANCE QUALIFICATIONS A levels/Scottish Highers required: 1/2 in science subjects preferred. Grade: C or above. **Other entry qualifications:** Most qualifications equivalent to A levels considered. **Mature applicants:** There is a flexibility towards mature students. **STUDENT NUMBERS Annual applications:** 40 (1994). **Annual places:** 10 (1994). **EMPLOYMENT ENTERED:** Successful graduates gain exemption from part 1 of professional law training and are able to enter the legal profession. **COURSE PROFILE:** The programme combines study of six core law courses (law of contract, constitutional and administrative law, criminal law, law of torts, land law, law of trusts), together with environmental law, intellectual property law, biotechnology and conservation. **FUTURE DEVELOPMENTS:** A postgraduate course in Environmental Management for business is planned.

THE UNIVERSITY OF BUCKINGHAM
Environmental Biology
BSc 2 years (4 terms/year) Full-time

ENTRANCE QUALIFICATIONS GCSEs/SCEs required: Maths grade C, biology and chemistry or combined science. A levels/Scottish Highers preferred: At least one science subject, biology or chemistry. Grade: C or above. **Other entry qualifications:** Most equivalent qualifications considered. Mature applicants: a flexible approach. **STUDENT NUMBERS Annual applications:** 150 (1994). **Annual places:** 15 (1994). **EMPLOYMENT ENTERED:** Postgraduate courses, NRA, water industry, other industry, MAFF. **COURSE PROFILE:** Broad based first year covering most areas of biology. Specialist option in final year, including substantial environmental research project and courses in conservation and environmental biology.

UNIVERSITY OF CENTRAL ENGLAND IN BIRMINGHAM
Environmental Planning
BSc (Hons) 3 Years Full-time + 1 Year Postgraduate Diploma in Town & Country Planning (Part-time available)

ENTRANCE QUALIFICATIONS: Although no qualifications are strictly necessary those without other experience should have five GCSE subjects of which two are at A level or four GCSE subjects of which three are at A, including maths and English. Geography and social science subjects also preferred. **Other entry qualifications:** Other qualifications including ONC, OND, GNVQ and BTEC, as well as relevant 'life experience' are taken into account. **STUDENT NUMBERS Annual applications:** 350 (1994). **Annual places:** 50 (1994). **EMPLOYMENT ENTERED:** Local planning authorities, national parks authorities, private sector (eg planning advisors for super-market chains). **COURSE PROFILE:** The course aims to provide a broad education in the critical analysis and interpretation of, and policy recom-mendations relating to a range of social, economic and environmental subjects and issues. Final year specialisms include: urban regeneration, natural resource management, urban design and conservation, transport and communications and European planning.

CHELTENHAM AND GLOUCESTER COLLEGE OF HIGHER EDUCATION
Environmental Policy
BSc/BA 3 Years (or more part-time) Full- and Part-time

CHESTER COLLEGE OF HIGHER EDUCATION
Applied Biology
Diploma in Higher Education 2 Years Full-time

ENTRANCE QUALIFICATIONS: Any two A levels/Scottish Highers/Irish Highers. **Other entry qualifications:** One GNVQ, three AS levels, BTEC, Access Courses and Open College units also considered. Interviews with the course leader. **STUDENT NUMBERS Annual applications:** 40 (1994). **Annual places:** 27 (1994). **EMPLOYMENT ENTERED:** Environmental industries (eg NRA), food industries (eg food sciences, retailing) **COURSE PROFILE:** Initial modules of the course are more general, covering: biology, physical science and earth science. Later modules include: microbiology, biochemistry, ecology and environmental chemistry. Modu-lar system means that students can adapt the course to suit their own interests. Modules in information technology and a work placement are also included. **FUTURE DEVELOPMENTS:** Addition of a third year for conversion to BSc Environmental Studies.

COVENTRY UNIVERSITY
Environmental Science
BSc 3 Years Full-time or 4 Years Full-time with European study or 4 Year sandwich

ENTRANCE QUALIFICATIONS GCSEs/SCEs required: Maths, English and at least one science. GCSEs/SCEs preferred: Biology, chemistry and/or geography. A level/Scottish Higher required: Biology. A levels/Scottish

Highers preferred: Chemistry, physics, geography, geology, maths, statistics and/or languages. Grade: Five B Grades at Scottish higher level. **Other entry qualifications:** OND (with at least five Merits in specified subjects), HI-TECH Foundation, Open Access to Science, OU S102. **Mature applicants:** Strongly encouraged subject to interview/discussion **STUDENT NUMBERS Annual applications:** 350 (1994). **Annual places:** 35 (1994). **EMPLOYMENT ENTERED:** Postgraduate courses, environmental consultancy, technical and scientific research posts (inc. NRA, MAFF, British Sugar Corporation), conservation bodies etc. **COURSE PROFILE:** The course concentrates on studies of the physical and biotic components of the natural environment and the first year includes a foundation in the earth and life sciences, plus statistics and computing. The second and third years have core modules in ecology and resource management and specialisation options in; pollution and ecotoxicology, water resources, historical environments, agricultural systems, biological conservation and environmental law. Importance is attached to practical skills in techniques of environmental monitoring, analysis and interpretation.

CRANFIELD UNIVERSITY – SILSOE COLLEGE
Environmental Engineering (Land & Water)
BEng (Hons) Optional Sandwich Full-time

ENTRANCE QUALIFICATIONS GCSEs/SCEs required: Maths, English and at least one science. A levels/Scottish Highers required: Three A levels or four Scottish Highers including maths and a physical science subject, science subjects preferred. Scottish Highers grade B. **Other entry qualifications:** Most equivalent, suitable qualifications considered. **Mature applicants:** Considered on an individual basis. **STUDENT NUMBERS Annual places:** 6 (1994). **EMPLOYMENT ENTERED:** Planning and water authorities, mineral abstractors, large estates, amenity & leisure developers, conservation bodies. **COURSE PROFILE:** Engineering science and material, graphics and surveying, computing, engineering maths and statistics, fluid mechanics, geology and land use, engineering structures and materials, river engineering, plant/soil environment engineering, operational control, landscape engineering, earth moving, site management. Industrial placements available.

CRANFIELD UNIVERSITY – SILSOE COLLEGE
Environment Management
BSc (Hons) 4 Year Sandwich Full-time

ENTRANCE QUALIFICATIONS GCSEs/SCEs required: Maths, English, one Science subject. GCSEs/SCEs preferred: Biology, chemistry, economics A levels/Scottish Highers required: Two A levels in suitable subjects, three preferred. Four Scottish Highers. A levels/Scottish Highers preferred: environmental science, biology, chemistry, economics, geography, physics, maths, geology, business studies. Grade: Scottish Higher grades BBCC. **Other entry qualifications:** A range of equivalent, suitable qualifications considered. **Mature applicants:** are considered on an individual basis. **STUDENT NUMBERS Annual places:** 20 (1994). **EMPLOYMENT ENTERED:** National parks, water authorities, environment protection agencies, local government countryside or recreation departments, land managing and conservation charities (RSPB), waste disposal companies. **COURSE PROFILE:** Ecology, plant science, microbiology, soils and geomorphology, air photo interpretation, environmental issues, IT, surveying & graphics, business studies, landscape design, habitat assessment, forestry and woodland management, countryside recreation, field machinery, waste and pollution control technology, hydro and water technology, environmental law, EIS, rural policy, EIA, field course. Industrial placements available.

CRANFIELD UNIVERSITY – SILSOE COLLEGE
Environmental Technology
BSc (Hons) 4 Years Sandwich Full-time

ENTRANCE QUALIFICATIONS GCSEs/SCEs required: Maths, English and one science. A levels/Scottish Highers required: Two A levels in suitable subjects compulsory three preferred, four Scottish Highers. A levels/Scottish Highers preferred: Environmental science, biology, chemistry, geography, physics, technology and maths. Grade: Scottish Higher grades BBCC. **Other entry qualifications:** A range of equivalent, suitable qualifications considered. **Mature applicants:** Considered on an individual basis. **EMPLOYMENT ENTERED:** New course. **COURSE PROFILE:** Microbiology and ecology, soil and plant science, IT, surveying, graphics, hydrology and hydrogeology, soil and plant environmental engineering, waste and pollution control technology, environment monitoring, water table control, habitat creation, EIA, landscape engineering, business studies, conservation management, economics and policy, field courses, research project.

CRANFIELD UNIVERSITY – SHUTTLEWORTH COLLEGE
Business Management and the Environment
BSc (Hons) 4 Year Sandwich Full-time

ENTRANCE QUALIFICATIONS GCSEs/SCEs required: Maths, English and one Science. A levels/Scottish Highers required: At least two A levels or four Scottish Highers in suitable subjects. Grade: Scottish Higher Grades

BBCC. **Other entry qualifications:** BTEC National Diploma with Merit in at least three relevant subjects, relevant advanced GNVQ plus a variety of other equivalent qualifications considered. **Mature applicants:** All considered on an individual basis. **STUDENT NUMBERS Annual places:** 20 (1994). **EMPLOYMENT ENTERED:** Marketing, sales personnel, finance & accounts, health & safety, planning, distribution, customer services, commerce, education, the food industry, production, land & estate management. **COURSE PROFILE:** Business organisations, accounts and finance, IT, global issues, economics and business environment, human resource management, marketing, business legislation, environmental policy, energy management, water management, waste and pollution control, environmental impact assessment, environmental monitoring, environmental management systems, environmental legislation, final year project. The course includes industrial placements.

UNIVERSITY COLLEGE STOCKTON
Environmental Development
BSc (Hons) 3 Years Full-time Dip HE 2 Years Full-time Certificate 1 Year Full-time (Part-time available).

ENTRANCE QUALIFICATIONS: For full-time degree courses GCSE English plus GCSE/SCE passes in five subjects including two at A level or GCSE/SCE passes in four subjects including three at A levels (N.B. two AS levels maybe offered in place of each A level). **Other entry qualifications:** Kite-marked Access courses, CATS, BTEC or SCOTVEC, Open University, School leaving qualifications obtained Eire and in many other countries. **Mature applicants:** Welcome. **STUDENT NUMBERS Annual applications:** 37 (1994). **Annual places:** 20 (1994). **EMPLOYMENT ENTERED:** Industry, the public sector, conservation, education or regulating bodies. Focusing on the relationship between people and ecosystems. Semester-based, the program is arranged in modules.

UNIVERSITY COLLEGE STOCKTON
Environmental Management
BSc 3 Years Full-time Dip HE 2 Years Full-time Certificate 1 Year Full-time (Part-time available)

ENTRANCE QUALIFICATIONS For full-time Degree courses GCSE/SCE English plus GCSE/SCE passes in five subjects including two at A level, or GCE/GCSE passes in four subjects including three at A level. (N.B. two AS levels may be offered in place of each A level). **Other entry qualifications:** Kite-marked Access Courses, CATS, BTEC or SCOTVEC, Open University Credits, School-Leaving Qualifications obtained in Eire and in many other countries. **Mature Applicants:** Welcome. **STUDENT NUMBERS Annual applications:** 71 (1994). **Annual places:** 35 (1994). Industry, the public sector, conservation, education or regulating bodies. **COURSE PROFILE:** Focusing on the practical management of the environment in order to reconcile the pressures between use and conservation. Semester-based, the programme is arranged in modules.

UNIVERSITY COLLEGE STOCKTON
Environmental Technology
BSc (Hons) 3 Years Full-time Dip HE 2 Years Full-time Certificate 1 Year Full-time (Part-time available)

ENTRANCE QUALIFICATIONS: For full-time degree courses GCSE English plus GCSE/SCE passes in five subjects including two at A level or GCSE/SCE passes in four including three at A levels. (N.B. two AS levels may be offered in place of each A level). Grades: N/A. **Other entry qualifications:** Kite-Marked Access Courses, CATS, BTEC or SCOTVEC, Open University Credits, School leaving qualifications obtained in Eire and in many other countries. **STUDENT NUMBERS Annual applications:** 49 (1994). Annual places: 22 (1994). **EMPLOYMENT ENTERED:** Industry, the public sector, conservation, education or regulating bodies. **COURSE PROFILE:** Focusing on how we can repair and prevent environmental damage. Students will have the opportunity to spend a one year work placement in a local company or public sector organisation. Semester-based, the programme is arranged in modules.

DE MONTFORT UNIVERSITY BEDFORD
Science and the Environment
BSc 4 Years (Sandwich) Full-time

DE MONTFORT UNIVERSITY BEDFORD
Environmental Studies/ Biology
BA/BSc 3 Years Full-time (Part-time available)

ENTRANCE QUALIFICATIONS GCSEs/SCEs preferred: Maths and English. A levels/Scottish Highers required: 10 points. **Other entry qualifications:** All other qualifications considered. **Mature Applicants:** Welcome. **STUDENT NUMBERS Annual applications:** 160 (1994). **Annual places:** 32 (1994). **EMPLOYMENT ENTERED:** Postgraduate studies, local government, teaching, industry. **COURSE PROFILE:** Year 1 provides a basic understanding of natural and social systems and introduces ecology, geography and socio-economic sustainability. In year 2 more global environmental issues are featured and year 3 focuses on the management and planning of environments. Year 3 also incorporates an individual project.

UNIVERSITY OF DUNDEE
Environmental Science
BSc 3/4 Years Full-time

ENTRANCE QUALIFICATIONS GCSEs/SCEs required: Biology and geography. A levels/Scottish Highers required: two or three A levels, three or four Scottish Highers depending on grades. Grade: A levels BC or CCD, Scottish Highers BBB or BBCC. Mature students: Treated flexibly. **STUDENT NUMBERS Annual applications:** 110 (1994). **Annual places:** 20 (1994). **EMPLOYMENT ENTERED:** Environmental consultancy, pollution control, river purification boards, water resource management (NRA), conservation. **COURSE PROFILE:** Multidisciplinary courses from years 1–4 with a strong emphasis on geoscience, remote sensing, and ecology. Taught by the departments of geography, biological sciences, chemistry, applied physics and civil engineering. **FUTURE DEVELOPMENTS:** Plans are being made to provide new joint courses in Environmental Science & Chemistry and Environmental Science & Physics.

UNIVERSITY OF DUNDEE
Environmental Science Joint Hons
MA 3/4 years Full-time

ENTRANCE QUALIFICATIONS GCSEs/SCEs required: Chemistry, biology or physics, geography a preferred subject. A Levels/Scottish Highers preferred: Geography or biology. Grade: A Levels BCC. Scottish Highers BBBC. **Other entrance qualifications:** Mature applicants welcome. **STUDENT NUMBERS Annual applications:** 200 (1994). **Annual places:** 20 (1994). **EMPLOYMENT ENTERED:** Environmental assessment, planning, tourist development, general management training programmes. **COURSE PROFILE:** This is a joint degree with another social science subject. Environmental Science is multidisciplinary and largely taught by Geography and Biological Sciences, but with certificates from Chemistry, Applied Physics and Civil Engineering.

UNIVERSITY OF EAST ANGLIA
Environmental science
BSc 3 Years Full-time

ENTRANCE QUALIFICATIONS GCSEs/SCEs required: Maths. GCSEs/ SCEs preferred: Range of science subjects. A levels/Scottish Highers preferred: Two from a biological subject, chemistry, geology, economics, geography, environmental sciences, maths, physics, physical sciences. Scottish Higher grades required: AABB. **Mature Applicants:** applications considered on an individual basis. **STUDENT NUMBERS Annual applications:** 700 (1994). Annual places: 75 (1994). **EMPLOYMENT ENTERED:** Research, teaching (geology, geophysics, oceanography, hydrology, meteorology, soil science, planning), professions.

UNIVERSITY OF EAST LONDON
Animal Biology
BSc (Hons) 3/4 Years Sandwich Full-time or Part-time

ENTRANCE QUALIFICATIONS GCSEs/SCEs required: Maths and English. GCSEs/SCEs preferred: Biology, chemistry or double science. A levels/Scottish Highers required: two suitable subjects at A level including at least one science subject. A levels/Scottish Highers preferred: four subjects at Scottish Higher including two science subjects. Grade: Cs. **Other entry qualifications:** BTEC ND, AS, GNVQ (science), Baccalaureate, Access (science). **Mature Applicants:** Considered on an individual basis: Background and experience taken into consideration. **STUDENT NUMBERS Annual applications:** 80 (1994). **Annual places:** 20 (1994). **EMPLOYMENT ENTERED:** Posts at Institute of Ophthalmology, hospital technical officers, and teaching. **COURSE PROFILE:** The course covers the diversity, evolution, biology and ecology of the animal kingdom. The final year places special emphasis on parasitology and entomology.

UNIVERSITY OF EAST LONDON
Applied Ecology
BSc (Hons) 3/4 Years Sandwich Full-time or Part-time

ENTRANCE QUALIFICATIONS GCSEs/SCEs required: Maths and English. GCSEs/SCEs preferred: Biology, chemistry or double science. A levels/Scottish Highers required: two suitable subjects at A Level including one science, four suitable subjects at Scottish Higher level including two sciences. Biology the preferred subject. Grade: Cs. **Other entry qualifications:** BTEC ND, A/S, GNVQ (science), Baccalaureate, Access (science). **Mature students:** Are considered on an individual basis with their background and experience taken into consideration. **STUDENT NUMBERS Annual applications:** 20 (1994). **Annual places:** 10 (1994). **EMPLOYMENT ENTERED:** Rothampsted Experimental Station, Epping Forest Environmental Services. **COURSE PROFILE:** A scientific approach to the study of animal and plant populations/communities. The course includes substantial field study.

UNIVERSITY OF EAST LONDON
Environmental Sciences
BSc (Hons) 3/4 Years Sandwich Full-time or Part-time

ENTRANCE QUALIFICATIONS GCSEs/SCEs required: Maths and English. GCSEs/SCEs preferred: Biology, chemistry or double science. A levels/Scottish Highers required: two A levels including at least one science subject four Scottish Highers including two science subjects. Biology being the preferred subject. Grade: Cs. **Other entry qualifications:** BTEC ND, AS, GNVQ (science), Baccalaureate, Access (science). **Mature applicants:** Considered on an individual basis: Background and experience taken into consideration. **STUDENT NUMBERS Annual applications:** 60 (1994). **Annual places:** 20 (1994). **EMPLOYMENT ENTERED:** New course. **COURSE PROFILE:** The course offers a broad study of environmental topics and techniques. Options include environmental management, pollution, conservation, biological monitoring, prehistoric and historic environmental law, politics, policy and many others.

UNIVERSITY OF EAST LONDON
Environmental studies
BSc/BA (Hons) 3/4 Years Sandwich Full-time or Part-time

ENTRANCE QUALIFICATIONS GCSEs/SCEs required: Maths and English. A levels/Scottish Highers required: two suitable subjects at A level four suitable subjects at Scottish Higher. A level/Scottish Higher grades required: C. **Other entry qualifications:** BTEC ND, GNVQ, Baccalaureate, Access. **Mature applicants:** Considered on an individual basis: Background and experience taken into account. **STUDENT NUMBERS Annual applications:** 80 (1994). Annual places: 20 (1994). **EMPLOYMENT ENTERED:** New course. **COURSE PROFILE:** An examination of the relationship between people and the environment, involving a better understanding of our planet, its resources, its animals and plants. Studies range from the prehistoric environment to the current state of the world in terms of lifestyle, sociology, politics and law.

UNIVERSITY OF EAST LONDON
Wildlife Conservation
BSc (Hons) 3/4 Years Sandwich Full-time or Part-time

ENTRANCE QUALIFICATIONS GCSEs/SCEs required: Maths and English. GCSEs/SCEs preferred: Biology, chemistry or double science. A levels/Scottish Highers required: two suitable A level subjects including at least one science, four subjects at Scottish Higher including two science subjects. A levels/Scottish Highers preferred: Biology. A level/Scottish

Higher grades required: C. **Other entry qualifications:** BTEC ND, AS, GNVQ (science), Baccalaureate, Access (science). **Mature applicants:** Considered on an individual basis: Background and experience taken into account. **STUDENT NUMBERS Annual applications:** 95 (1994). **Annual Places:** 30 (1994). **EMPLOYMENT ENTERED:** New course. **COURSE PROFILE:** A course for those with an active interest in natural history and wildlife conservation. The course covers basic environmental biology, ecology, biological conservation, animal and insect diversity, the environment and the law, environmental pollution and field study techniques.

UNIVERSITY OF GLAMORGAN
Environment and Social Values (Green Studies)
BA (Hons) 3 Years Full-time

ENTRANCE QUALIFICATIONS GCSEs/SCEs required: Maths or science, English. GCSEs/SCEs preferred: Open. A levels/Scottish Highers required: two A level passes in any subject area and their Scottish equivalent. A level/Scottish Higher grades required: Open. **Other entry qualifications**: BTEC (three Merits at level III), GNVQ (level III). Mature applicants: Required to supply alternative evidence of suitability if normal criteria are not fulfilled. **STUDENT NUMBERS Annual applications:** 85 (1994). **Annual places:** 22 (1994). **EMPLOYMENT ENTERED:** New course. **COURSE PROFILE:** This is an interdisciplinary degree scheme, which gains its uniqueness by offering a broad based educational experience to those interested in studying environmental issues from a philosophical and sociological perspective.

UNIVERSITY OF GLAMORGAN
Environmental Pollution Science
BSc (Hons) 3/4 Years Thick Sandwich Full-time

ENTRANCE QUALIFICATIONS GCSEs/SCEs required: Maths grade C or above. GCSEs/SCEs preferred: Chemistry, biology, physics grade C. A levels/Scottish Highers preferred: At least one from chemistry, biology, physics, environmental science. **Other entry qualifications:** OND in science or engineering, other ONDs or Certs with 3 level III Merits, Access (science). **Mature applicants:** Must be able to demonstrate necessary motivation. **STUDENT NUMBERS Annual applications**: 100 (1994). **Annual places:** 43 (1994). **EMPLOYMENT ENTERED:** Water companies, NRA, environmental consultancies, British Steel. **COURSE PROFILE:** Several themes throughout course including: environmental chemistry and analysis, environmental ecology and microbiology, conservation and management. May include thick sandwich industrial placement.

UNIVERSITY OF GLAMORGAN
Energy and Environmental Technology
BSc (Hons) 3/4 Years Thick Sandwich Full-time

ENTRANCE QUALIFICATIONS GCSEs/SCEs required: Maths and a science subject. A levels/Scottish Highers preferred: Any two A levels. **Other entry qualifications:** If relevant 3 Merits at level III. **Mature applicants:** Qualifications and relevant experience taken into consideration. **STUDENT NUMBERS Annual places:** 15 (1994). **EMPLOYMENT ENTERED:** Enforcement agencies, industry/service sector (environmental officers/auditors), Health & Safety. **COURSE PROFILE:** Modular course includes open learning. Students are able to specialise in final year of module. The final year projects are similar to small work placements. **FUTURE DEVELOPMENTS:** Course review in 1995 – more emphasis to be placed on environmental management, auditing and impact.

GLASGOW CALEDONIAN UNIVERSITY
Energy and Environmental Technology
BSc (Hons) 4 Years Full-time

ENTRANCE QUALIFICATIONS GCSEs/SCEs required: Maths and one science subject. GCSEs/SCEs preferred: English, additional science subjects. A levels/Scottish Highers required: Maths. A levels/Scottish Highers preferred: Minimum of two A levels or three Highers English and science subjects. A level/Scottish Higher grades required: Cs. **Other entry qualifications:** All other qualifications considered. **Mature applicants:** Interview and negotiation. **STUDENT NUMBERS Annual applications:** 100+ (1994). **Annual places:** 26 (1994). **EMPLOYMENT ENTERED:** New course. **COURSE PROFILE:** Environmental knowledge comes from interdisciplinary study of science and technology along with an understanding of social sciences, economics and law. Graduates will be technically skilled and be able to participate in identifying and resolving environmental problems.

UNIVERSITY OF GREENWICH
Environmental Sciences
BSc (Hons) 3/4 Years Sandwich Full-time or Part-time

ENTRANCE QUALIFICATIONS GCSEs/SCEs required: Maths and English. GCSEs/SCEs preferred: A selection of subjects from the natural and social sciences. A levels/Scottish Highers required: two A levels, three Scottish Highers in natural and social sciences. A level/Scottish Higher grades required: Cs. **Other entry qualifications:** BTEC ND in Science/Technology with 50% Merit at level III, GNVQ (science with Merits),

Access. **Mature applicants:** A wide range of possible qualifications and experience can be considered in support of your application. **STUDENT NUMBERS** Annual applications: 444 (1994). Annual places: 87 (1994). **EMPLOYMENT ENTERED:** Conservation, environmental planning, management and protection, London boroughs, Women's Environmental Network, Shropshire Trust For Nature Conservation, Community Connection. **COURSE PROFILE**: We offer a multi-disciplinary approach to environmental understanding. The course seeks to integrate aspects of social, physical and natural sciences. During year 1 the emphasis is on foundation knowledge and skills. In years 2 and 3 there is emphasis on global and regional issues, together with environmental philosophy, policy and legislation. The practical aspects of environmental analysis, management and protection are also important. **FUTURE DEVELOPMENTS:** Expand the ERASMUS network – to be joined by new partners. MSc Environmental Conservation is to be offered from October 1995.

UNIVERSITY OF GREENWICH
Environmental Control
BSc (Hons) 3 Years Full-time

ENTRANCE QUALIFICATIONS GCSEs/SCEs required: Maths, English and one science. GCSEs/SCEs preferred: Sciences. A levels/Scottish Highers preferred: Physics, chemistry, maths. A level/Scottish Higher grades required: Cs minimum. **Other entry qualifications:** Qualifications equivalent to A levels considered. **Mature applicants:** Welcome. Interview prior to acceptance. **STUDENT NUMBERS Annual applications:** 444 (1994). **Annual places:** 90 (1994). **EMPLOYMENT ENTERED:** Local authorities, regulatory bodies (NRA, HMIP), industry, water companies, environmental consultancies. **COURSE PROFILE:** General first year covering basics of environmental studies – science and society; maths, computing and statistics. Specialised study in 2nd/3rd years of environmental monitoring, analysis, legislation, energy and water industries. Final year specialisms in EIA and environmental management and auditing.

GWENT COLLEGE OF HIGHER EDUCATION
Environmental Studies with Geography/European Studies
BA (Hons) 3 Years Full-time or Part-time

ENTRANCE QUALIFICATIONS GCSEs/SCEs required: English. GCSEs/SCEs preferred: Biology, geography, maths. **Other entry qualifications:** BTEC with environmental component. **Mature applicants:** Policy very flexible. **STUDENT NUMBERS Annual applications:** 40 (1994). **Annual places:** 35 (1994). **EMPLOYMENT ENTERED:** Local government (planning, housing, environment), country parks, forestry, water companies, private sector environmental agencies. **COURSE PROFILE:** The approach is holistic and integrated. Units include ecology, biostatics, environmental biology, aquatic/terrestrial environments, conservation, philosophy and ethics, waste management. Wide scope for individual projects. Case studies from Severnside and Black Mountain, also third world and global issues. Some industrial placements available.

GWENT COLLEGE OF HIGHER EDUCATION
Environmental Systems
BA 3 Years Full-time or 6 Years Part-time

HARPER ADAMS COLLEGE
Rural Environmental Protection
BSc/BSc (Hons) 4 Years Sandwich Full-time

ENTRANCE QUALIFICATIONS GCSEs/SCEs required: five GCSEs. GCSEs/SCEs preferred: Maths, English, double science or science subject. A levels required: 8 points. A level/Scottish Higher preferred: Science. Scottish Higher grades required: CCCC or above. **Other entry qualifications:** BTEC ND, Certificate or equivalent. **Mature applicants:** Considered with appropriate experience and on merit. **STUDENT NUMBERS Annual applications:** 120 (1994). **Annual places:** 34 (1994). **EMPLOYMENT ENTERED:** New course. **COURSE PROFILE:** The course has three main strands – wildlife/conservation, agriculture and the socio-economics of the rural environment. Graduates will have the skills to minimise or prevent environmental problems arising out of agricultural practises and rural leisure activities.

UNIVERSITY OF HERTFORDSHIRE
Combined Modular Scheme in Environmental Science
BSc (Hons) 3 Years Full-time

ENTRANCE QUALIFICATIONS GCSEs/SCEs required: Maths and English. A levels/Scottish Highers preferred: one Science. **Other entry qualifications:** OND/ONC, AS, GNVQ, Baccalaureate all accepted. **Mature applicants:** Normally interviewed. **STUDENT NUMBERS Annual applications:** 150+ (1994). **Annual places:** 35 (1994). **EMPLOYMENT ENTERED:** Research officers for various trusts, scientific officers (NRA), woodland management, teaching, further study. **COURSE PROFILE:** Encourages an integrated scientific understanding of the environment with particular emphasis being placed on the ability to monitor environmental change and propose and implement solutions. **FUTURE DEVELOPMENTS:** BSc Environmental Geology.

UNIVERSITY OF HERTFORDSHIRE – WEST HERTS. COLLEGE
Environmental Studies
BSc 4 Years sandwich Full-time

UNIVERSITY OF HULL
Environmental Resources and Management
BSc 3 Years Full-time or Part-time

ENTRANCE QUALIFICATIONS GCSEs/SCEs required: Maths and English. A levels/Scottish Highers preferred: Economics, geography or biology, geography. A level/Scottish Higher grades required: Negotiable. **Mature applicants:** Entry qualifications negotiable. **STUDENT NUMBERS Annual applications:** 150+ (1994). **Annual places:** 15 (1994). **EMPLOY-MENT ENTERED:** Local government, environmental consultancy, industry. **COURSE PROFILE:** This course combines elements of environmental policy and practise with management, economics and science (optional), to offer an inter-disciplinary approach.

UNIVERSITY OF HUMBERSIDE
Environmental Studies
BA (Hons) 3 Years Full-time Optional Sandwich Year

ENTRANCE QUALIFICATIONS GCSEs/SCEs required: Minimum of three subjects at grade C or above. GCSEs/SCEs preferred: Biology, geography, maths, chemistry, English, economics. A levels/Scottish Highers preferred: Biology, geography, economics, chemistry, humanities and science equally acceptable. Scottish Higher grades required: CCCC. **Other entry qualifications:** All qualifications considered on merit including Access and overseas qualifications. **Mature applicants:** Very much encouraged. Flexible entry requirements. Advanced entry may be possible for mature students with prior experience/qualifications. **STUDENT NUMBERS Annual applications:** 300 (1994). **Annual places:** 60 (1994). **COURSE PROFILE:** The course is interdisciplinary and explicitly acknowledges the role of human activity in shaping the environment. The course incorporates human geography, business, policy, economics, and management as well as science and technology. Field work, both in the UK and abroad form a strong element. Opportunities for study overseas are available.

UNIVERSITY OF LONDON – IMPERIAL COLLEGE
Civil and Environmental Engineering
MEng 4 years Full-time

ENTRANCE QUALIFICATIONS GCSEs/SCEs preferred: English. A levels required: 3 including maths and physics. Scottish Highers required: 5

including maths and physics or CSYS maths and physics, compulsory. Grade: Scottish Highers grade A in maths and physics plus three B grades. **Other entrance qualifications:** Other qualifications will be considered on an individual basis. **STUDENT NUMBERS Annual applications:** 600+ **Annual places:** 75 (1994). **EMPLOYMENT ENTERED:** Civil engineering consultancies and contractors, local authorities and postgraduate courses. **COURSE PROFILE:** A sound basis in civil engineering is laid down in the first two and a half years. The final eighteen months involve a programme of elective subjects and an end-of-studies project, both of which provide for an environmental specialisation. The course is also available with a year in Europe, for which the student must have a GCSE, grade A or B, in the appropriate language.

UNIVERSITY OF LONDON – IMPERIAL COLLEGE
Environment and Earth Resources Engineering
MEng 4 years Full-time

ENTRANCE QUALIFICATIONS GCSEs/SCEs required: English. A levels/Scottish Highers required: three A levels including maths or physics, chemistry and/or biology also preferred Grade: Scottish Higher grades BBBBC **Other entrance qualifications:** Other experience and qualifications considered on an individual basis. **STUDENT NUMBERS Annual applications:** 30 (1994). **Annual places:** 15 (1994). **EMPLOYMENT ENTERED:** Mining and quarrying companies (eg RTE, Tarmac), oil companies (eg Shell, BP), regulatory and local authorities (eg NRA), consultancy companies. **COURSE PROFILE:** This four year MEng degree aims to produce high quality, professional environmental engineers with specialised knowledge of the mineral and petroleum raw materials industry. Subjects studied include; basic engineering topics, environmental chemistry, earth sciences, mineral and chemical engineering, environmental law and social aspects. Industrial placements are encouraged, but not compulsory.

KEELE UNIVERSITY
Environmental Management
BA 3 Years Full-time

ENTRANCE QUALIFICATIONS GCSEs/SCEs required: Maths and English – Cs. Scottish Higher grades required: BBBC. **Other entry qualifications:** Most other relevant qualifications considered. **Mature applicants:** Welcomed. Must be 19 years or over and been away from full-time education for 3 years. Interview likely. **STUDENT NUMBERS Annual applications:** 458 (1994). **Annual places:** 40 (1994). **EMPLOYMENT ENTERED:** New course. **COURSE PROFILE:** Course taught jointly by

ENVIRONMENTAL MANAGEMENT at KEELE UNIVERSITY

A three-year modularized degree course at Keele University, Staffordshire, providing a multidisciplinary approach to the management of the political, economic, legal and social factors affecting our environment today.

Course outline:

Year 1: – Environmental Management: Contexts and Debates, The Natural Environment, Economics for E.M., Principles of Environmental Law.

Year 2: – Evaluating Environments, Environmental Economics, Environmental Policy.

Year 3: – Ecological Economics, a dissertation selected by the student, and two special subject modules again selected by the student.

The course forms part of Keele's modularized Dual Honours degree scheme, with students reading two Principal subjects; Environmental Management, together with one from a list of some 25 others – this approach providing Keele graduates with a broad-based education which equips them well for future careers.

For further information please contact:

The Head of Environmental Management, Department of Geography, Keele University, Keele, Staffordshire ST5 5BG. *Tel. 01782 583160.*

departments of geography and economics with subsidiary inputs from law, international relations and politics. Provides an integrated, cross disciplinary approach to environmental management.

KING ALFRED'S COLLEGE
Combined Studies (including environmental studies)
BSc/BA 3 Years Full- or Part-time

LANCASTER UNIVERSITY
Environmental Science
BSc 3 Years Full-time

ENTRANCE QUALIFICATIONS GCSEs/SCEs required: English and maths, integrated science or individual physics and chemistry preferred. A levels/Scottish Highers required: At least one from maths, physics, chemistry and/or engineering science, at least one from geography, geology and/or biology preferred. Grade: A level grades BBC, Scottish Higher grades BBBBB. **Other entry qualifications:** AS levels, BTEC, ONC/OND, International/European Baccalaureate, OU S102 and Access to Sciences Course also considered. Mature applicants: encouraged. **STUDENT NUMBERS Annual Applications:** 410 (1994). **Annual places:** 45 (1994). **EMPLOYMENT ENTERED:** Scientific industrial services (inc. environmental planning, construction consultants), public scientific services (inc. Institute of Hydrology), teaching, postgraduate training and research. **COURSE PROFILE:** This is an interdisciplinary course which applies physical, chemical, numerical and managerial methods to the study of the natural and human environments. The course is delivered in a modular form and therefore has inherent flexibility.

LANCASTER UNIVERSITY
Environmental Chemistry
BSc 3 Years Full-time

ENTRANCE QUALIFICATIONS GCSEs/SCEs required: Maths and English. A levels/Scottish Highers required: Chemistry. Maths, biology and/or physics preferred. Grade: A-level grades CCC/CCD, Scottish Higher grades BBBCC. **Other entry qualifications:** BTEC merits, International Baccalaureate (28 points) also considered. **Mature applicants:** Enquiries from mature students welcome. **STUDENT NUMBERS Annual applications:** 81 (1994). **Annual places:** 20 (1994). **EMPLOYMENT ENTERED:** NRA, HMIP etc. **COURSE PROFILE:** Environmental Chemistry is an integrated, self-contained, interdisciplinary course with modules in chemistry, environmental science, environmental chemistry, biology and ecology. It is NOT a chemistry course with final year options in environmental chemistry. **FUTURE DEVELOPMENTS:** Introduction of a North American exchange scheme where the undergraduates can spend the second year at a North American university.

LANCASTER UNIVERSITY
Ecology
BSc (Hons) 3 Years Full-time

ENTRANCE QUALIFICATIONS GCSEs/SCEs required: English and maths, chemistry preferred. A levels/Scottish Highers required: At least two from biology, chemistry, physics, maths and/or geography compulsory, other subjects considered for third A-level. Grade: Scottish Highers five B grades or above. **Other entry qualifications:** OND, ONC, AS levels, GNVQ, International Baccalaureate and Access Course qualifications also considered, all students are considered on an individual basis. **Mature applicants:** Should be able to demonstrate evidence of recent study and a relevant background eg practical experience. **STUDENT NUMBERS: Annual applications:** c. 200. **Annual places:** 30 (1994). **EMPLOYMENT**

ENTERED: Higher degrees, research, teaching, conservation, national parks, local authority environmental posts, industry (inc. water and electricity industries), environmental consultancy. **COURSE PROFILE:** An integrated ecology course emphasising the interactions between the physical environment and the biological components. Considerable emphasis on practical ecology and its applications, involving considerable fieldwork throughout years two and three. Flexibility allows considerable scope for individual specialisation.

LANCASTER UNIVERSITY
Environmental Management
BSc 3 Years Full-time

ENTRANCE QUALIFICATIONS GCSEs/SCEs required: Maths (grade A or B), English and one other from physics, chemistry or integrated science (grade C or above). A levels/Scottish Highers required: one science subject and two others. Grade: Scottish Highers five B grades or above. **Other entry qualifications:** Full consideration is given to other qualifications (inc. International Baccalaureate 30 points), and relevant experience and training. **STUDENT NUMBERS: Annual Applications:** 200 (1994). **Annual Places:** 20 (1994). **EMPLOYMENT ENTERED:** New course. **COURSE PROFILE:** The course offers scientific insight into processes effecting the environment and its management, along with consideration of the social, legal and policy implications of environmental changes. This is the only UK degree covering the environmental sciences and human application of environmental change.

LANCASTER UNIVERSITY
Environmental Mathematics
BSc 3 Years Full-time

ENTRANCE QUALIFICATIONS GCSEs/SCEs required: Physical science or integrated science (grade B or above). A levels/Scottish Highers required: Maths (A level grade B or CSYS maths). **Other entry qualifications:** BTEC with Distinction in three relevant subjects, International Baccalaureate 30 points including higher maths. **Mature applicants:** Considered on individual merits. **STUDENT NUMBERS Annual applications:** 22 (1994). **Annual places:** 6 (1994). **EMPLOYMENT ENTERED:** New course. **COURSE PROFILE:** Environmental Mathematics offers a combination of courses chosen to give a strong foundation in both environmental science and mathematics, together with advanced skills in statistical methods, systems and control. The scheme includes a full-scale project and a range of options.

LANCASTER UNIVERSITY
Environmental Systems Engineering
BEng/MEng BEng 3 Years Full-time MEng 4 Years Full-time

ENTRANCE QUALIFICATIONS GCSEs/SCEs required: Maths, English and physics, chemistry preferred. A levels/Scottish Highers required: Maths and one science subject, particularly physics, preferred. Grade: Scottish Higher grades: BEng BBBBB, MEng AABBB. **Other entry qualifications:** OND, HNC, AS levels, BTEC with level III maths distinction, International Baccalaureate BEng 30 points, MEng 32 points. **Mature applicants:** Welcome, special consideration given for relevant experience. **STUDENT NUMBERS Annual applications:** 50 (1994). **Annual places:** 5 (1994). **EMPLOYMENT ENTERED:** New course. **COURSE PROFILE:** The course aims to produce engineers capable of designing and manufacturing products beneficial to the environment. The course achieves this by providing students with the necessary fundamental knowledge in engineering and environmental science.

UNIVERSITY OF LEEDS
Environmental Management
BA 3 Years Full-time

ENTRANCE QUALIFICATIONS GCSEs/SCEs required: Maths (grade B), economics preferred. A levels/Scottish Highers required: Geography compulsory, maths and economics preferred. Grade: Scottish Higher grades BBBCC. **Other entry qualifications:** AS levels and International Baccalaureate also considered. Mature applicants: Interviewed. **STUDENT NUMBERS Annual applications:** 215 (1994). **Annual places:** 33 (1994). **COURSE PROFILE:** The course has an emphasis on geography, economics, law and related political and sociological areas, with basic science and engineering aspects developed to allow understanding of environmental problems. A wide choice of options, via a modular structure, permits specialisation, including European and developing nations dimensions.

UNIVERSITY OF LEEDS
Environmental Science: Energy Option
BSc 3 Years Full-time

ENTRANCE QUALIFICATIONS A levels/Scottish Highers required: Chemistry or maths. **STUDENT NUMBERS Annual applications:** 120 (1994). **Annual places:** 15 (1994). **EMPLOYMENT ENTERED:** First graduates 1996. **COURSE PROFILE:** The course covers the basic science of energy and combustion together with the environmental impacts of energy use and environmental protection.

UNIVERSITY OF LEEDS
Environmental Science: Biogeoscience Option
BSc 3 Years Full-time

ENTRANCE QUALIFICATIONS A levels/Scottish Highers required: Biology and geography, another science and/or and maths preferred. Grade: Scottish Higher grades AABBB. **Other entry qualifications:** AS levels and International Baccalaureate considered. **Mature applicants:** Interviews for mature applicants. **STUDENT NUMBERS Annual applications:** 325 (1994). **Annual places:** 20–25. **COURSE PROFILE:** The course is based on geology, geography and pure and applied biology, the choice of modules allows students to emphasise one or two of these aspects. Basic environmental management and engineering content is developed to a level which allows wider understanding of problems, including legal, ethical ad economic aspects.

UNIVERSITY OF LEEDS
Environmental Science: Environmental Chemistry Option
BSc 3 Years Full-time

ENTRANCE QUALIFICATIONS: GCSEs/SCEs and A levels/Scottish Highers required: Chemistry. Geography, geology, biology, maths and environmental science preferred subjects. Grade: Scottish Higher grades BBBCC. **Other entry qualifications:** AS levels, International Baccalaureate, BTEC and Access Courses considered. **Mature applicants:** Interviewed. **STUDENT NUMBERS Annual applications:** 170 (1994). **Annual places:** 20 (1994). **EMPLOYMENT ENTERED:** First graduates 1995. **COURSE PROFILE:** The course emphasises chemical aspects, including natural processes and pollution, affecting water, air and land. The modular structure allows a wide choice for developing interests in biology, geography and energy science. Basic management and engineering aspects are developed to facilitate understanding of environmental problems.

UNIVERSITY OF LIVERPOOL
Environmental Physical Sciences
BSc 3 Years Full-time

ENTRANCE QUALIFICATIONS GCSEs/SCEs required: Maths, English and sciences (dual award or at least two including chemistry). A levels/ Scottish Highers required: Chemistry, physics, maths, biology or geography preferred. Scottish Higher grades required: ABBBB. **Other entry qualifications:** AS level, BTEC and International Baccalaureate all acceptable, other qualifications considered on individual merit. **Mature applicants:** Mature students considered on individual merits, Access Courses are acceptable. **STUDENT NUMBERS: Annual applications:** 120 (1994). **Annual places:** 10 (1994). **COURSE PROFILE:** The course provides a multi-disciplinary approach to environmental science, with an emphasis on the chemical and physical aspects. Core skills are developed in environmental analysis, using 'hands-on' experience of modern instrumental methods.

UNIVERSITY OF LONDON – BIRKBECK COLLEGE
Environmental Conservation/Environmental science
BSc 4 Years Part-time

ENTRANCE QUALIFICATIONS: Flexible entry qualifications for mature students. **STUDENT NUMBERS Annual applications:** 30. **Annual places:** 20. **EMPLOYMENT ENTERED:** Environmental control, countryside management, environmental law. **COURSE PROFILE:** Both degree courses share some programmes in common. The BSc Environmental Conservation studies the causes and consequences of the ecological and environmental changes of present and long-term trends. The BSc Environmental Science concentrates on the purely scientific aspects of environmental issues.

UNIVERSITY OF LONDON – KING'S COLLEGE
Applied Environmental Science
BSc 4 Years (inc. year placement) Full-time or Part-time

STUDENT NUMBERS: Annual applications: 142 (1994). **Annual places:** 17 (1994). **EMPLOYMENT ENTERED:** Environmental consultancy, nature reserve wardens, English Nature, NRA, the media, publishing, law. **COURSE PROFILE:** The course has the same basic content as the Human Environmental Science BSc, with all the flexibility and opportunities to specialise offered by that course, but with the addition of a year placement (during the third year) in an environmental setting. **FUTURE DEVELOPMENTS:** Increasing input of earth science and human geography options, ranging from environmental management to remote sensing.

UNIVERSITY OF LONDON – KING'S COLLEGE
Human Environmental Science
BSc 3 Years Full-time or Part-time

ENTRANCE QUALIFICATIONS GCSEs/SCEs required: Combined science, chemistry and/or biology. GCSEs/SCEs preferred: Maths. A levels/Scottish Highers required: Biology. A levels/Scottish Highers preferred: Chemistry and/or maths. A level/Scottish Higher grades required: Scottish Higher grades BBCCC. **Other entry qualifications:** OND with five final year Merits, AS levels as supplement to compulsory A level, International

Baccalaureate with a 5/7 average. **STUDENT NUMBERS Annual applications:** 102 (1994). **Annual places:** 16 (1994). **EMPLOYMENT ENTERED:** Environmental consultancy, nature reserve warden, English Nature, NRA, the media, publishing, law. **COURSE PROFILE:** The course combines the study of the natural environment with an understanding of current human impact. A flexible module system allows specialisation in topics ranging from ecological conservation and water resource management to ecotoxicology and pollution control. **FUTURE DEVELOPMENTS:** Increasing input of earth science and human geography options, ranging from environmental management to remote sensing.

UNIVERSITY OF LONDON – ROYAL HOLLOWAY
Biology with Environmental Studies
BSc 3 Years Full-time

ENTRANCE QUALIFICATIONS GCSEs/SCEs required: Maths. GCSEs/SCEs preferred: Integrated science or individual sciences (particularly chemistry and/or physics). A levels/Scottish Highers required: Biology. A levels/Scottish Highers preferred: Geography and/or chemistry. A level/Scottish Higher grades required: Scottish Higher grade B biology, plus four grade C or above. **Other entry qualifications:** one A level may be substituted by two AS levels. Irish Leaving Certificate or International Baccalaureate acceptable. Mature applicants: Considered with an approved Science Access or Science Foundation course. **STUDENT NUMBERS Annual applications:** 42 (1994). **Annual places:** 10 (1994). **EMPLOYMENT ENTERED:** New course. **COURSE PROFILE:** This degree is taught in modules, allowing flexibility and opportunity to pick up appropriate courses in a number of departments including geography, geology, physics and social policy. The fieldwork element is strong in all years. A project concerning environmental issues can be undertaken in the third year if required.

UNIVERSITY OF LONDON – ROYAL HOLLOWAY
Environmental Biology
BSc 3 Years Full-time

ENTRANCE QUALIFICATIONS GCSEs/SCEs required: Maths. GCSEs/SCEs preferred: Integrated science or individual sciences (particularly chemistry and physics). A levels/Scottish Highers required: Biology. A levels/Scottish Highers preferred: Chemistry or another science and/or geography. A level/Scottish Higher grades required: Scottish Higher grade B biology, plus four grade C or above. **Mature applicants:** Considered with an approved Science Access or Science Foundation course. **STUDENT**

NUMBERS Annual applications: 88 (1994). **Annual places:** 20 (1994). **EMPLOYMENT ENTERED:** Research at universities and with NRA, environmental research consultancies etc. **COURSE PROFILE:** The degree is taught in course units to allow flexibility. fieldwork elements are strong in both biology and geography. Environmental problems are considered both at home and abroad, and the third year includes an environmental project.

UNIVERSITY OF LONDON – ROYAL HOLLOWAY
Environmental Geochemistry
BSc 3 Years Full-time

ENTRANCE QUALIFICATIONS GCSEs/SCEs required: English, maths plus combined science (double) or chemistry. GCSEs/SCEs preferred: Geography and/or geology. A levels/Scottish Highers required: Chemistry. A levels/Scottish Highers preferred: Physics, maths, biology, geology, environmental science and/or geography. **Other entry qualifications:** All qualifications considered, all applicants interviewed. **STUDENT NUMBERS Annual applications:** 15 (1994). **Annual places:** Flexible. **COURSE PROFILE:** The course covers the application of chemical principles to geological sciences in the environment, and includes; analytical geochemistry, hydrogeochemistry, fluid geochemistry, exploration techniques, pollution of soil and groundwater, waste disposal.

UNIVERSITY OF LONDON – ROYAL HOLLOWAY
Environmental Geology
BSc 3 Years Full-time

ENTRANCE QUALIFICATIONS GCSEs/SCEs required: English language, Maths plus combined science (double) or chemistry. GCSEs/SCEs preferred: Geography and/or geology. A levels/Scottish Highers required: One from physics, chemistry, biology, maths geology or environmental science. A levels/Scottish Highers preferred: Two more of the above subjects and/or geography. **Other entry qualifications:** All qualifications considered, all applicants interviewed. **STUDENT NUMBERS Annual applications:** 34 (1994). **Annual places:** Flexible. **EMPLOYMENT ENTERED:** Not known. **COURSE PROFILE:** The course covers the application of geological sciences to environmental issues, and includes: Impacts of natural hazards and the exploitation of natural resources, quarrying, mining, waste disposal, hydrogeology, urban geology, pollution of soil and groundwater.

UNIVERSITY OF LONDON – ROYAL HOLLOWAY
Geology with Environmental Studies
BSc 3 Years Full-time

ENTRANCE QUALIFICATIONS GCSEs/SCEs required: English language, maths plus combined science (double) or chemistry. GCSEs/SCEs preferred: Geology and/or geography. A level/Scottish Higher required: one from physics, chemistry, biology, maths, geology, geography or environmental science. A levels/Scottish Highers preferred: two more of the above subjects. **Other entry qualifications:** All qualifications considered, all applicants interviewed. **STUDENT NUMBERS Annual applications:** 18 (1994). **Annual places:** Flexible. **COURSE PROFILE:** The geological component of the degree (up to 75%) includes; rocks, minerals, fossils, structures, plate tectonics, palaeontology, physics and chemistry of the earth. The environmental component (25% plus) includes: ecology, energy, social policy, management, resources, waste disposal and environmental issues.

UNIVERSITY OF LONDON – UNIVERSITY COLLEGE LONDON
Environmental Geography
BSc 3 Years Full-time

ENTRANCE QUALIFICATIONS GCSEs/SCEs required: English and maths. A level required: Geography. A level preferred: one other science. Scottish Higher grades required: BBBCC **Other entry qualifications:** Other qualifications assessed on an individual basis. **Mature applicants:** With overall Merit in an Access course considered on an individual basis. **STUDENT NUMBERS Annual applications:** 118 (1994). **Annual places:** Up to 15. **EMPLOYMENT ENTERED:** Students on the standard BSc Geography degree have entered: environmental consultancy, English Nature, NRA. **COURSE PROFILE:** The course has an emphasis on scientific approaches to studying environmental systems and their management. There is a particular emphasis on environmental change in temperate, Mediterranean and sub-tropical areas and places importance on the translation of science into public policy.

UNIVERSITY OF LONDON – WYE COLLEGE
Environmental Science
BSc 3 Years (Sandwich available) Full-time

ENTRANCE QUALIFICATIONS GCSEs/SCEs required: Maths and English. GCSEs/SCEs preferred: Sciences. A levels/Scottish Highers required: None compulsory. A levels/Scottish Highers preferred: Biology or chemistry and two others. A level/Scottish Higher grades required: N/A.

Other entry qualifications: Qualifications equivalent to above considered. Mature applicants: Welcomed subject to demonstration of satisfactory study skills eg Access (Merit grade). **STUDENT NUMBERS Annual applications:** 140 (1994). **Annual places:** 25–30 (1994). **EMPLOYMENT ENTERED:** NRA, chemical companies, ADAS, local authorities, teaching, further study. **COURSE PROFILE:** Practical lab based science training with emphasis on rural aspects. First year biology, ecology, chemistry, soils, statistics and project on estate. Second year entomology, pathology, ecology, pollution, soil, environmental impact assessment, sustainable agro and global change and project work. Third year lab or field based project and choice of supporting courses. **FUTURE DEVELOPMENTS:** The course content is constantly under review.

LONDON UNIVERSITY – WYE COLLEGE
Rural Environmental Studies
BSc (Hons) 3 Years Full-time

ENTRANCE QUALIFICATIONS GCSEs/SCEs required: Maths, English language. A level/Scottish Higher grades required: 18 points. **Other entry qualifications:** Other qualifications are assessed individually. **Mature applicants:** Keen to recruit mature students with suitable qualifications. **STUDENT NUMBERS Annual applications:** Not known. **Annual places:** 25 (1994). **EMPLOYMENT ENTERED:** Policy bodies, local authorities, English Nature, further education, research. **COURSE PROFILE:** The course looks at all aspects of the rural environment from the policy organisation and analysis perspective. It is global in orientation.

LONDON UNIVERSITY – WYE COLLEGE
Countryside Management
BSc (Hons) 3 Years Full-time

ENTRANCE QUALIFICATIONS GCSEs/SCEs required: Maths, English. A level/Scottish Higher grades required: 18 points. **Other entry qualifications:** Assessed on an individual basis. **Mature applicants:** Keen to recruit mature students with suitable qualifications. **STUDENT NUMBERS Annual places:** 25 (1994). **EMPLOYMENT ENTERED:** Countryside management, RSPB, Natural Trust, private estates, local authorities. **COURSE PROFILE:** The course is oriented towards the practicalities of management and management planning and focuses on Northern Europe and North America.

LONDON GUILDHALL UNIVERSITY
Environmental Policy and Management
BA 3 Years Full-time (Part-time study possible)

ENTRANCE QUALIFICATIONS GCSEs/SCEs required: English. GCSEs/SCEs preferred: Maths, biology, geography. A levels/Scottish Highers required: None. A levels/Scottish Highers preferred: Any of geography, economics, sociology, politics. **Mature applicants:** Encouraged to apply, each case being considered individually, currently about 50% of entrants are mature. **STUDENT NUMBERS Annual applications:** c.120. **Annual places:** 40. **COURSE PROFILE:** This course takes a multi-disciplinary approach to environmental policy making and management, combining geography, economics, politics and sociology. **FUTURE DEVELOPMENTS:** Environmental law and business units to be incorporated into the course.

LOUGHBOROUGH UNIVERSITY OF TECHNOLOGY
Chemical Engineering and Environmental Protection
BSc (Hons) 3/4 Years Sandwich Full-time

ENTRANCE QUALIFICATIONS GCSEs/SCEs required: Maths. GCSEs/SCEs preferred: Physics, chemistry. A levels/Scottish Highers required: Maths. A levels/Scottish Highers preferred: Physics, chemistry. A level/Scottish Higher grades required: N/A. **Other entry qualifications:** HND, Baccalaureate. **Mature applicants:** Will consider individual applicants on merit. **STUDENT NUMBERS Annual applications:** 650 (1994). **Annual places:** 78 (1994). **EMPLOYMENT ENTERED:** Process industries, process design, construction companies. **COURSE PROFILE:** The course is essentially a chemical engineering one with emphasis on environmental control and protection aspects. It enjoys full accreditation by the Institute of Chemical Engineers. **FUTURE DEVELOPMENTS:** The course will switch to a modular form and be given in two semesters per year from 1995.

UNIVERSITY OF MANCHESTER
Environmental Studies
BA 5 Years for Ordinary 6 Years for Hons Part-time

ENTRANCE QUALIFICATIONS GCSEs/SCEs preferred: English language, geography, biology, environmental science. **Mature applicants:** Each student interviewed and considered on own merit taking into account qualifications and experience. **COURSE PROFILE:** Processes and problems of change in the physical, social and economic environments of both urban and rural areas in the developed and developing world. Lab sessions, fieldwork, projects and essays important compliments to the lectures, seminars and tutorials.

UNIVERSITY OF MANCHESTER
Environmental and Resource Geology
BSc 3 Years Full-time

ENTRANCE QUALIFICATIONS GCSEs/SCEs required: English language, double science or chemistry. A levels/Scottish Highers preferred: Science subjects. A level/Scottish Higher grades required: CCC/BBBBB or 18 points. **Other entry qualifications:** Welcomed and considered individually. **Mature applicants:** All applications considered. Science based Access courses preferred. **STUDENT NUMBERS Annual applications:** 93 (1994). **Annual places:** 20 (1994). **COURSE PROFILE:** This is a geology degree with an environmental bias. It involves substantial field work, including a five week independent mapping project. The course is linked to the Greater Manchester Geological Unit which provides earth science advice to planners/developers. **FUTURE DEVELOPMENTS:** When students take time out of the course they are encouraged and helped to find relevant industrial experience.

UNIVERSITY OF MANCHESTER
Environmental Science
BSc 3 Years Full-time

ENTRANCE QUALIFICATIONS GCSEs/SCEs preferred: Maths, sciences. A levels/Scottish Highers required: A Science subject. A levels/Scottish Highers preferred: Other sciences, maths, geography, geology. A level/Scottish Higher grades required: CCC/BBBBB or 18 points. **Other entry qualifications:** Other qualifications considered individually. **Mature applicants:** All applicants considered individually. Science based Access course necessary. **STUDENT NUMBERS Annual applications:** New course. **Annual places:** 10 (1995). **COURSE PROFILE:** The major strength is the emphasis on the engineering aspects of dealing with the environment.

UNIVERSITY OF MANCHESTER
Environmental Studies
BSc 3 Years Full-time

ENTRANCE QUALIFICATIONS GCSEs/SCEs preferred: Maths, geography, a science. A levels/Scottish Highers preferred: Geography, chemistry, maths or any arts subject. A level/Scottish Higher grades required: CCC/BBBBB or 18 points. **Other entry qualifications:** Other qualifications welcomed and considered individually. **Mature applicants:** All applicants considered individually. Science based Access Course preferred. **STUDENT NUMBERS Annual applications:** New course. **Annual places:** 10 (1995). **COURSE PROFILE:** This will be broadly based with more emphasis on economic, legal and planning issues as relating to the environment. Engineering is less prominent in this course.

UNIVERSITY OF MANCHESTER INSTITUTE OF SCIENCE & TECHNOLOGY
Environmental Chemistry
BSc (Hons) 3 Years Full-time

ENTRANCE QUALIFICATIONS GCSEs/SCEs required: Chemistry, physics, maths, or double science, English – minimum grade C. A levels/Scottish Highers required: Chemistry. **Mature applicants:** Welcomed and considered on their own merits for either three year or four year (incorporates two year HND) course. **STUDENT NUMBERS Annual applications:** 36 (1994). **Annual places:** 7 (1994). **COURSE PROFILE:** Core chemistry covered in years 1 and 2. Final year covers 12 modules relating to environmental chemistry. Two subsidiary subjects in years 1 and 2 are chosen with bearing on final year specialism. Four year course involves 3rd year in industrial placement or study abroad (language taught in years 1 and 2) followed by final year environmental chemistry modules is possible.

MANCHESTER METROPOLITAN UNIVERSITY
Environmental Management
BSc 3 Years Full-time 4-7 Years Part-time

ENTRANCE QUALIFICATIONS GCSEs/SCEs required: Maths, English. A levels/Scottish Highers preferred: Geography, economics, sciences (especially biology/chemistry). A level/Scottish Higher grades required: 16 points. **Other entry qualifications:** Alternative entry qualifications accepted/ encouraged including Access. Possible direct entry into level two with HND etc. in appropriate subject areas. **Mature applicants:** Interviewed. **STUDENT NUMBERS Annual applications:** 650. **Annual places:** 50. **EMPLOYMENT ENTERED:** Local authorities (environmental, planning, recreation/ leisure), national bodies, Groundwork Trusts, voluntary bodies, environmental consultancy, water authorities, nature conservation. **COURSE PROFILE:** Combined academic knowledge, skills development and vocational training. Core units include management, planning, economics, life and physical sciences. Electives available including languages. Two compulsory placements (UK and/or international).

MANCHESTER METROPOLITAN UNIVERSITY
Environmental Science
BSc 3/7 Years Full-time or Part-time

ENTRANCE QUALIFICATIONS GCSEs/SCEs required: English, maths, chemistry. A levels/Scottish Highers preferred: Minimum of two Sciences. **Other entry qualifications:** BTEC, OND, ONC etc. **Mature applicants:** Usually by interview. **STUDENT NUMBERS Annual applications:** 700. **Annual places:** 45. **COURSE PROFILE:** A science course dealing with the natural environment and progressing to applications in the field of human activities. Specialisms in conservation, agriculture, water pollution, energy, earth science and land management.

MANCHESTER METROPOLITAN UNIVERSITY
Environmental Studies (Single subject and part of a combined studies degree)
BSc 3 Years Full-time and Part-time

ENTRANCE QUALIFICATIONS GCSEs/SCEs required: Maths and English. A levels/Scottish Highers required: 14–16 points. **Other entry qualifications:** Acceptable. **Mature applicants:** Welcome – relevant experience, interests and recent study an advantage. **STUDENT NUMBERS Annual applications:** 1500. **Annual places:** 55. **EMPLOYMENT ENTERED:** Local authorities (planning, pollution control), teaching/environmental education and interpretation, conservation organisations. **COURSE PROFILE:** The central concern is for the maintenance and improvement of the quality of the environment (and life) through the interaction of scientific, technical, economic and cultural factors. Thus it reflects the current public awareness of, and concern for, environmental issues.

MIDDLESEX UNIVERSITY (In association with Capel Manor Horticultural and Environmental Centre)
Environmental and Business Management
BA (Hons) 3 Years Full-time

ENTRANCE QUALIFICATIONS GCSEs/SCEs required: Biology or geography, maths, science. GCSEs/SCEs preferred: Economics, biology, geography, business studies, environmental science. A levels/Scottish Highers required: Biology or geography, maths, science. A levels/Scottish Highers preferred: Economics, geography, biology, business studies, environmental science. **STUDENT NUMBERS Annual applications:** Not available. **Annual places:** Not available. **EMPLOYMENT ENTERED:** Environmental trusts, local authorities, environmental coordinators. **COURSE PROFILE:** Develops business and environmental skills and a balanced understanding of the needs of business and the environment. Emphasises practical skills through work related action projects.

NAPIER UNIVERSITY
Environmental Biology
BSc/BSc (Hons) 3/4 Years Sandwich optional 5th Year Full-time

ENTRANCE QUALIFICATIONS GCSEs/SCEs required: English, maths, chemistry. GCSEs/SCEs preferred: Biology. A levels/Scottish Highers required: Either chemistry or biology. Scottish Higher grades required: BCC (one sitting) BBCC or BBB (two sittings). **Other entry qualifications:** ONC, OND, IB, BTEC. **Mature applicants:** Candidates 21 or over who do not meet entry requirements may be accepted as long as they have recent and relevant industrial experience. **STUDENT NUMBERS Annual applications:** Not available. **Annual places:** 30 (1994). **COURSE PROFILE:** The course includes topics such as metabolic process in organisms, chemistry of major pollutants, an ecological consideration of how differences in the ways organisms interact with their environment, affect survival and reproduction, monitoring, analysis, management and conservation of resources, influence of human activity.

NESCOT – EPSOM COLLEGE OF HIGHER & FURTHER EDUCATION
Applied Ecology
BSc (Hons) 3 Years Full-time

ENTRANCE QUALIFICATIONS GCSEs/SCEs preferred: Maths and English. A levels/Scottish Highers required: One science, geography or environmental studies. A levels/Scottish Highers preferred: Biology, chemistry. A level/Scottish Higher grades required: N/A. **Other entry qualifications:** BTEC ND/NC in science, GNVQ in science, Access course. **Mature applicants:** Relevant learning and/or experience will be considered by a college accreditation of prior learning procedure. applicants welcome. **STUDENT NUMBERS Annual places:** 20 (1995). **COURSE PROFILE:** The first year provides a broad base of biology and ecology. The second year specialises in more advance aspects of ecology, including man's impact on the environment. The final year contains applied subjects such as conservation and pollution plus a practical project. **FUTURE DEVELOPMENTS:** New course.

NESCOT
Environmental Management
BSc 3 Years Full-time 5 Years Part-time

ENTRANCE QUALIFICATIONS GCSEs/SCEs preferred: English, maths and science. A levels/Scottish Highers required: One science subject or geography or environmental science or similar. A levels/Scottish Highers preferred: Biology, chemistry, geography, environmental science. **Other**

Environmental Science

Epsom's college
of higher and
further
education

Nescot,
Reigate Road
Ewell, Epsom
Surrey
KT17 3DS

Switchboard
0181 394 1731

Fax
0181 394 3030

*Nescot offers the following undergraduate and postgraduate
full-time and part-time courses in Environmental Science:*

- HNC in Pollution Management (F/T & P/T)
- HNC in Environmental Health (P/T)
- HND in Environmental Monitoring & Control (F/T)
- BSc in Applied Ecology (F/T)
- BSc in Environmental Health (P/T)
- BSc in Environmental Management (F/T & P/T)
- MSc in Acoustics (F/T & P/T)
- Diploma of the Institute Acoustics (P/T)

For further details on all courses contact Dr John Osborn, Faculty
of Science & Technology, Nescot, Reigate Road, Ewell, Epsom,
Surrey, KT17 3DS. **Telephone 0181 394 3101/3099/3111**

Nescot

entry qualifications: BTEC ND/NC in Science, Access course. **Mature
applicants:** Mature students who do not meet entrance requirements can
gain entry to the course in accordance with college APL procedure.
STUDENT NUMBERS Annual applications: 20 (1994). **Annual places:** 20
(1994). **EMPLOYMENT ENTERED:** New course. **COURSE PROFILE:**
The course is modular and highly vocational covering the following major
areas: ecology and conservation, environmental monitoring, pollution
sources, effects and control methodologies, environmental policy. law,
economics and management, occupational health & hygiene, environmental modelling, waste management.

UNIVERSITY OF NEWCASTLE UPON TYNE
Environmental Biology
BSc (Hons) 3 Years Full-time

ENTRANCE QUALIFICATIONS GCSEs/SCEs required: Maths, English.
GCSEs/SCEs preferred: A language, a science or combined science subject,
geography. A levels/Scottish Highers required: Biology. A levels/Scottish

Highers preferred: Chemistry or maths. A level/Scottish Higher grades required: AABB. **Other entry qualifications:** All considered. **Mature applicants:** Relevant experience and motivation taken into account. **STU-DENT NUMBERS Annual applications:** 120 (1994). **Annual places:** 15 (1994). **EMPLOYMENT ENTERED:** New course. **COURSE PROFILE:** Biological processes in terrestrial, freshwater and marine ecosystems, emphasising interactions of organisms with their surroundings: Community ecology, biological conservation, ecophysiology, ecotoxicology, environmental micro-biology, global processes and climate change, plant animal interactions.

UNIVERSITY OF NEWCASTLE UPON TYNE
Agriculture and Environmental Science
BSc (Hons) 3 Years Full-time

ENTRANCE QUALIFICATIONS GCSEs/SCEs required: Maths. GCSEs/ SCEs preferred: Chemistry, biology, geography. A levels/Scottish Highers required: biology – A level, biology and chemistry – Highers. A levels/ Scottish Highers preferred: chemistry, biology, geography. Scottish Higher grades required: BBBB. **Other entry qualifications:** HND, AS, GNVQ, Irish Highers, Access, Baccalaureate, International Baccalaureate. **Mature applicants:** All considered on individual merits. **STUDENT NUMBERS Annual applications:** 350 (1994). **Annual Places:** 63 (1994). **EMPLOYMENT ENTERED:** Both the agricultural and environmental industries, environmental consultancies, environmental protection agencies. **COURSE PRO-FILE:** Integration of the scientific problems of food production with environmental considerations. Wide choice of modules.

UNIVERSITY OF NEWCASTLE UPON TYNE
Agriculture and Environmental Science – Agricultural Zoology
BSc (Hons) 3 Years Full-time

ENTRANCE QUALIFICATIONS GCSEs/SCEs required: Maths. GCSEs/ SCEs preferred: Chemistry, biology, geography. A levels/Scottish Highers required: Biology – A level, biology and chemistry – Highers. A levels/ Scottish Highers preferred: Chemistry, geography, biology. Scottish Higher grades required: BBBB. **Other entry qualifications:** HND, AS, GNVQ, Irish Highers, Access, Baccalaureate, International Baccalaureate. **Mature applicants:** Welcomed, all considered on individual merits. **STUDENT NUMBERS Annual applications:** 350 (1994). **Annual Places:** 63 (1994). **EMPLOYMENT ENTERED:** Both the agricultural and environmental industries, environmental consultancies, environmental protection agencies. **COURSE PROFILE:** Biology and ecology of animals which have a beneficial or harmful effect on agriculture. How to encourage the beneficial and discourage the harmful in environmentally acceptable ways. Not the study of farm animals.

UNIVERSITY OF NEWCASTLE UPON TYNE
Agriculture and Environmental Science – Plant Science
BSc (Hons) 3 Year Full-time

ENTRANCE QUALIFICATIONS GCSEs/SCEs required: Maths. GCSEs/ SCEs preferred: Chemistry, biology, geography. A levels/Scottish Highers required: Biology – A level, biology and chemistry – Highers. A levels/ Scottish Highers preferred: Chemistry, geography, biology. Scottish Higher grades required: BBBB. **Other entry qualifications:** HND, AS, GNVQ, Irish Highers, Access, Baccalaureate, International Baccalaureate. **Mature applicants:** Welcomed, all considered on individual merits. **STUDENT NUMBERS Annual applications:** 350 (1994). **Annual places:** 63 (1994). **EMPLOYMENT ENTERED:** Both the agricultural and environmental industries, environmental consultancies, environmental protection agencies. **COURSE PROFILE:** Physiology, biochemistry, genetics, ecology, breeding, pests and disease of crop plants in relation to environmental concerns relating to excessive use of nitrogen and of chemical pesticides and herbicides.

UNIVERSITY OF NEWCASTLE UPON TYNE
Agriculture and Environmental Science – Soil Science
BSc (Hons) 3 Years Full-time

ENTRANCE QUALIFICATIONS GCSEs/SCEs required: Maths. GCSEs/ SCEs preferred: Chemistry, biology, geography. A levels/Scottish Highers required: Biology – A level, biology and chemistry – Highers. A levels/ Scottish Highers preferred: Chemistry, geography, biology. Scottish Higher grades required: BBBB. **Other entry qualifications:** HND, AS, GNVQ, Irish Highers, Access, Baccalaureate, International Baccalaureate. **Mature applicants:** Welcomed, all considered on individual merits. **STUDENT NUMBERS Annual applications:** 350 (1994). **Annual places:** 63 (1994). **EMPLOYMENT ENTERED:** Both the agricultural and environmental industries, environmental consultancies, environmental protection agencies. **COURSE PROFILE:** Study of soil as a resource in both natural and agricultural ecosystems in both temperate and tropical climates. Management and conservation of land, sustainable use of non-renewable resources, organic approaches.

UNIVERSITY OF NEWCASTLE UPON TYNE
Agriculture and Environmental Sciences – Terrestrial Ecology
BSc (Hons) 3 Years Full-time

ENTRANCE QUALIFICATIONS GCSEs/SCEs required: Maths. GCSEs/SCEs preferred: Chemistry, biology, geography. A levels/Scottish Highers required: Biology – A level, biology and chemistry – Highers. A levels/Scottish Highers preferred: Chemistry, geography, biology. Scottish Higher grades required: BBBB. **Other entry qualifications:** HND, AS, GNVQ, Irish Highers, Access, Baccalaureate, International Baccalaureate. **Mature applicants:** Welcomed, all considered on individual merits. **STUDENT NUMBERS Annual applications:** 350 (1994). **Annual places:** 63 (1994). **EMPLOYMENT ENTERED:** Both the agricultural and environmental industries, environmental consultancies, environmental protection agencies. **COURSE PROFILE:** Study of land plants and animals both wild and domesticated in relation to each other and to their environments. Both natural and managed ecosystems are examined. Conservation and environmental impact assessment.

UNIVERSITY OF NEWCASTLE UPON TYNE
Natural Resources
BSc 3 Years Full-time

ENTRANCE QUALIFICATIONS GCSEs/SCEs required: Maths, grade C or above. GCSEs/SCEs preferred: Additional science subjects to complement these at a more advanced level. A levels/Scottish Highers required: At least two subjects (three Scottish Highers) from natural science, technology, engineering or socio-economics. Scottish Higher grades required: BBBB. **Other entry qualifications:** two AS levels may be offered in place of one A level. International Baccalaureate: 26 points in appropriate subjects, GNVQ advanced level and appropriate additional studies accepted. **Mature applicants:** 10% of the intake are mature. Access Course qualifications accepted. **STUDENT NUMBERS Annual applications:** 60 (1994). **Annual places:** 20 (1994). **EMPLOYMENT ENTERED:** NRA, agricultural development overseas, conservation bodies, teaching. **COURSE PROFILE:** The course offers a broad training in the biological and earth sciences, together with an introduction to economics. It deals particularly with terrestrial ecosystems and those affecting them (ie climate, land, plants and animals, recreational use of land). **FUTURE DEVELOPMENTS:** The degree is currently being reviewed with changes to be introduced for the year 1995/96. Changes will make the degree structure more focused on management of terrestrial ecological resources and include a study of the exploitation of terrestrial resources.

UNIVERSITY OF NEWCASTLE UPON TYNE
Environmental and Ecological Engineering
BEng 3/4 Years Full-time

ENTRANCE QUALIFICATIONS GCSEs/SCEs required: Maths, physics, chemistry (or combined science), English. GCSEs/SCEs preferred: Biology. A levels/Scottish Highers required: Maths. A levels/Scottish Highers preferred: Physics, chemistry. Scottish Higher grades required: BBBB. **Other entry qualifications:** BTEC. **Mature applicants:** Encouraged to apply and considered individually (usually invited for interview). **STUDENT NUMBERS Annual applications:** 40 (1994). **Annual places:** 10 (1994). **EMPLOYMENT ENTERED:** Environmental protection agencies, environmental consultancy, process industry, mining and mineral extraction, land reclamation. **COURSE PROFILE:** The degree offers a route to a professionally recognised engineering qualification aimed at protection and remediation of the terrestrial environment. The curriculum integrates engineering principles with thorough exploration of ecology and environmental sciences.

NEWMAN COLLEGE
Geography and Environmental Science
BA Humanities 3 Years Full-time

ENTRANCE QUALIFICATIONS GCSEs/SCEs required: English. GCSEs/SCEs preferred: Maths. A levels/Scottish Highers required: Geography, environmental studies. **Other entry qualifications:** All considered. **Mature applicants:** Access course. **STUDENT NUMBERS Annual applications:** 160 (1994). **Annual places:** 80 (1994). **COURSE PROFILE:** Geography and environmental studies comprises about 25% of the degree, in which students choose three strands and follow a fourth. The geography strand provides modules on environmental systems, human and urban systems and environmental management.

NORTH EAST WALES INSTITUTE OF HIGHER EDUCATION
Environmental Studies
BA (Hons) 3 Years Full-time

ENTRANCE QUALIFICATIONS GCSEs/SCEs preferred: Maths, English. A levels/Scottish Highers preferred: From geography, biology/ecology, history, environmental studies/science, social science. A level/Scottish Higher grades required: DD (8 points). **Other entry qualifications:** OND/ONC, AS, OU Credits, GNVQ, BTEC, Access Course. **Mature applicants:** Welcome to apply, normally require at least five GCSEs or Access course. **STUDENT NUMBERS Annual applications:** 65 (1994).

newi

Athrofa Addysg Uwch Gogledd Ddwyrain Cymru
North East Wales Institute of Higher Education

University of Wales
Associated College

Environmental Degrees and BTEC HNDs

BA (Honours) Environmental Studies
BSc (Honours) Environmental Biology
BSc (Honours) Environmental Science
BSc (Honours) Estate Management
BSc (Honours) Quantity Surveying with Project Management

BTEC HND Building Studies (Architecture, Building Management, Quantity
        Surveying)
BTEC HND Environmental Sciences (awaiting validation)
BTEC HND Land Administration (Conservation and the Environment, Housing,
    Planning and Development or Valuation and Estate Management)

**Contact the Faculty Office for further information on (01978)
293099 or the Admissions Office on (01978) 293045**

FOUNDED IN 1975 FOR THE ADVANCEMENT OF HIGHER EDUCATION, TRAINING AND RESEARCH

Annual places: 25 (1994). **EMPLOYMENT ENTERED:** Planning and economic development, country park/heritage centre wardens, waste management/pollution control, primary and secondary school teaching, lecturing in FE, museum science, local government, retail management, nature conservation, civil service, environmental management. **COURSE PROFILE:** The course aims to enable students to appreciate the interface between the human environment and natural systems. It does so through the study of relevant principles and a critical evaluation of major environmental issues eg pollution, urban issues, rural issues. **FUTURE DEVELOPMENTS:** Students will have the option of completing parts of their second year course, and residential fieldwork in Tennessee, USA.

UNIVERSITY OF NORTH LONDON
Ecological Sciences
BSc 3 Years (4 Years Sandwich) Full-time and Part-time

ENTRANCE QUALIFICATIONS GCSEs/SCEs required: Maths, English. GCSEs/SCEs preferred: Science. A levels/Scottish Highers required: two science subjects. A levels/Scottish Highers preferred: Biology. A level/ Scottish Higher grades required: DD at A level, five passes including one B at Scottish Higher. **Other entry qualifications:** Access, OND/ONC, AS, Baccalaureate accepted in appropriate subjects. **Mature applicants:** All mature applicants are interviewed, more than half the students on the course are mature. **STUDENT NUMBERS Annual applications:** 40 (1994). **Annual places:** 16 (1994). **EMPLOYMENT ENTERED:** Conservation, ecological research, ecological administration, higher degrees. **COURSE PROFILE:** A modular course allowing great flexibility of choice in all years. There is a core of biological ecology to which may be added courses in biology, geography, chemistry and languages. **FUTURE DEVELOPMENTS:** Additional modules in freshwater ecology and ecological survey and monitoring.

UNIVERSITY OF NORTHUMBRIA AT NEWCASTLE
Environmental Management
BSc (Hons) 3 Years Full-time

ENTRANCE QUALIFICATIONS GCSEs/SCEs required: Maths, English. GCSEs/SCEs preferred: Sciences, geography. A levels/Scottish Highers required and preferred: three A levels including science and/or geography (C/D/E) or two A levels (B/D). Scottish Higher grades required: BBB. **Other entry qualifications:** Access/HEFC Courses – Credit/Merit levels, all A level equivalent courses considered. **Mature applicants:** Encouraged with appropriate work experience. **STUDENT NUMBERS Annual applications:** c. 600 (1994). **Annual places:** 45 (1994). **EMPLOYMENT ENTERED:** Postgraduate courses, teaching, environmental consultancy, NRA/water authorities, local councils – environmental policy, waste disposal, overseas – developing world projects. **COURSE PROFILE:** Environmental management and ecology focus in core part of course with wide selection of option choices eg environmental sustainability in the third world, remote sensing and resource assessment, strong input of staff research in local area and overseas – eg S. Spain and Africa. **FUTURE DEVELOPMENTS:** Possibility of BSc (Hons) Environmental Science Degree.

NOTTINGHAM TRENT UNIVERSITY
Combined Sciences
BSc 3 Years Full-time

NOTTINGHAM TRENT UNIVERSITY
Environmental Conservation and Management
BSc (Hons) 3 Years Full-time

ENTRANCE QUALIFICATIONS GCSEs/SCEs required: Maths. English.

A levels/Scottish Highers preferred: Biology, geography. Scottish Higher grades required: BBB. **Other entry qualifications:** All considered. **Mature applicants:** Very welcome, usually interviewed. **STUDENT NUMBERS Annual applications:** 350 (1994). **Annual places:** 70 (1994). **COURSE PROFILE:** Year 1: four core ECM, four core other subjects plus two supportive and two optional modules. Year 2: four core ECM, four core other subject, four optional modules, field course. Year 3: four core ECM, four core other subjects, two optional modules, project, field course.

UNIVERSITY OF PAISLEY
Environmental Science and Technology
BSc (Hons) 3 Years (BSc) 4 Years (BSc Hons) 5 Years Sandwich Full-time

ENTRANCE QUALIFICATIONS GCSEs/SCEs required: Chemistry, maths, English, (two GCSEs three SCEs) GCSEs/SCEs preferred: Biology, geography/geology. A levels/Scottish Highers required: Minimum of three Highers/two A levels in sciences. A levels/Scottish Highers preferred: Biology, chemistry. A level/Scottish Higher grades required: one science at grade B preferred. **Other entry qualifications:** All qualifications given credit status towards entrance, cases discussed individually. **Mature applicants:** Strongly encouraged to apply. Applications dealt with on an individual basis. **EMPLOYMENT ENTERED:** Manufacturing industry, research (industrial and academic), pollution inspectorate, river authorities, environmental consultancies, government institutes. **COURSE PROFILE:** Course designed to provide a sound training in environmental sciences with emphasis on the use of technology for problem solving. Industrial placement is optional in Honours course.

UNIVERSITY OF PLYMOUTH – SEALE HAYNE FACULTY
Agriculture And Countryside Management
BSc (Hons) 4 Years (Sandwich 1 Year) Full-time

ENTRANCE QUALIFICATIONS GCSEs/SCEs required: Science, English, maths. GCSEs/SCEs preferred: Biology, geography, chemistry. A levels/Scottish Highers required: two A levels, three Highers to include a science (geography accepted) 12 points. A levels/Scottish Highers preferred: Biology, geography, chemistry. Scottish Higher grades required: three Cs including one science. Other entry qualifications: ND in relevant environmental or business subject accepted – three Merits at final stage, Relevant HND may give direct entry to 2nd year. **Mature applicants:** Encouraged if have relevant experience in agriculture or countryside management – non-standard qualifications considered. **STUDENT NUMBERS Annual applications:** 140+ (1994). **Annual places:** 15 (1994). **EMPLOYMENT ENTERED:** Local authority, countryside management services, agricultural advisory and support industry. **COURSE PROFILE:** Modular degree with pathways in agriculture, business management and countryside management. First year provides background in relevant disciplines and IT, second year applied study, third year on placement (exemption possible), final year honours project and specialist options.

UNIVERSITY OF PLYMOUTH
Environmental Science
BSc (Hons) 3 Years Full-time

ENTRANCE QUALIFICATIONS GCSEs/SCEs required: five passes or equivalent including maths and English. A levels/Scottish Highers required: two A levels or equivalent including a science or mathematical subject. A level/Scottish Highers preferred: Geography or economics. **Other entry qualifications:** Extended science foundation year. **Mature applicants:** May be accepted with non-standard qualifications. **STUDENT NUMBERS Annual applications:** 725 (1994). **Annual places:** 126 (1994). **COURSE PROFILE:** Areas of specialism: biological, geological or social aspects. Final year options include conservation management, environmental monitoring, land reclamation and many more.

UNIVERSITY OF PLYMOUTH
Rural Resource Management
BSc (Hons) 4 Years Sandwich Full-time

ENTRANCE QUALIFICATIONS GCSEs/SCEs required: English, maths plus one other. A levels/Scottish Highers required: two A levels or 12 points. A level/Scottish Higher preferred: Science based including geography. **Other entry qualifications:** ND, Access courses. **Mature applicants:** welcomed. **STUDENT NUMBERS Annual applications:** 60 (1994). **Annual places:** 38 (1994). **EMPLOYMENT ENTERED:** Rangers/wardens in national parks, local authority county parks, nature reserves, National Trust and other voluntary bodies, officers in planning depts, water boards, tourist boards, Wildlife Trust, NRA, MAFF, NFU, environmental consultants. **COURSE PROFILE:** Specialist management of the rural environment. Course aims to provide students with the knowledge and skills to work in responsible and challenging careers in the countryside. The Faculty of Agriculture, Food and Land Use is based at Newton Abbot. The course makes full practical use of the South Devon examples of conflicting and complimentary land use and local resources.

UNIVERSITY COLLEGE OF RIPON AND YORK ST JOHN
Environmental Science with Management Studies
BSc (Hons) Combined Studies 3 Years Full-time

ENTRANCE QUALIFICATIONS GCSEs/SCEs required: English. If no A level biology then GCSE single subject science or dual award science at grade C or better. A levels/Scottish Highers preferred: Biology. Scottish Higher grades required: BBBB including English. **Other entry qualifications:** BTEC ND science with Merit in all subjects, GNVQ with Merit and appropriate additional units or one A level in appropriate subject, International Baccalaureate with 28 points including biology and English. **COURSE PROFILE:** Combined studies – 50% environmental science, 30% management studies, 20% work related studies and supporting studies.

UNIVERSITY COLLEGE OF RIPON AND YORK ST JOHN
Environmental Science with Geography
BSc (Hons) Combined Studies 3 Years Full-time

ENTRANCE QUALIFICATIONS GCSEs/SCEs required: English. If no A level biology then GCSE single subject science or dual award science at grade C or better. A levels/Scottish Highers required: Geography. A levels/Scottish Highers preferred: Biology. Scottish Higher grades required: BBBB including English. **Other entry qualifications:** BTEC ND science with Merit in all subjects, GNVQ with Merit and appropriate additional units or one A level in appropriate subject, International Baccalaureate with 28 points including biology and English. (All with A level geography). **Mature applicants:** Applicants welcome. Must pass Leeds University Mature Matriculation Examination if not in possession of normal entry requirements, or Access course. **STUDENT NUMBERS Annual applications:** 95 (1994). **Annual places:** 16 (1994). **COURSE PROFILE:** Combined studies – 50% environmental science, 30% management studies, 20% work related studies and supporting studies.

ROEHAMPTON INSTITUTE (UNIVERSITY OF SURREY)
Environmental Studies
BSc/BA (Hons) 3 Years Full-time or Part-time

ENTRANCE QUALIFICATIONS GCSEs/SCEs required: Maths and a science grade C or above. A levels/Scottish Highers required: two A levels or Highers preferably to include environmental science/studies. **Other entry qualifications:** All considered on merit. **Mature applicants:** Encouraged including Access. **STUDENT NUMBERS Annual applications:** 519 (1994). **Annual places:** 110 (1994). **EMPLOYMENT ENTERED:** Local authorities, central government (Inland Revenue, Housing, Environmental Health), postgraduate courses, research and professional training, retail trades, environmental analysis, leisure management. **COURSE PROFILE:** The course provides a compulsory foundation in geosystems, ecosystems, environmental science and techniques and an option from: the human impact, environmental problems, atmospheric systems. Honours level includes a compulsory field course and a wide choice from other modules. Advisory pathways provide career direction and specialisation. **FUTURE DEVELOPMENTS:** It is planned that the department will move to new accommodation in 1996.

ST ANDREWS UNIVERSITY
Environmental Geology
BSc 4 Years Full-time

ENTRANCE QUALIFICATIONS GCSEs/SCEs preferred: Science. A levels/Scottish Highers preferred: Science. Scottish Higher grades required: CCCCC or above. **Other entry qualifications:** Individuals need to discuss their qualifications with admission staff. **Mature applicants:** Need the same qualifications as school leavers. **STUDENT NUMBERS Annual applications:** 14 (1994). **Annual places:** 14 (1994). **COURSE PROFILE:** This is a modular course. After a common geoscience course for the first two years students take a pathway of modules selected from a core of environmental geology, environmental geophysics, applied geomorphology, land resources and optional modules form the geology, geography and geochemistry degrees.

UNIVERSITY OF SALFORD
1) Environmental Resources or 2) Environmental & Resource Science with Studies in Europe
BSc 3 Years Full-time or 4 Years Sandwich

ENTRANCE QUALIFICATIONS GCSE/SCE Preferred: Dual science, maths, geography, and foreign language if option 2) degree taken. A-levels/ Scottish Highers required: One relevant science subject (includes geography, environmental science/studies. Scottish Higher grades: BBCC in appropriate subjects. **Other entry qualifications:** BTEC OND/ONC three merits in appropriate subjects; two 'As' may be substituted for third 'A'; Advanced GNVQ at merit grade; Baccalaureate encouraged. **Mature applicants:** Welcomed and treated on an individual basis. Access certificate considered. **STUDENT NUMBERS Annual applications:** 300+. **Annual places:** 75. **COURSE PROFILE:** The course provides a holistic interdisciplinary, approach to environmental studies; scientific practises being integrated with relevant socio-environmental issues. Projects are essential elements of the programme. They are initiated by external agencies and involve real issues. 12 month placements offer opportunities throughout the UK and also overseas.

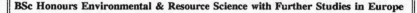
SCOTTISH AGRICULTURAL COLLEGE
Rural Business Management
BTechnol (Bachelor of Technology)/BTechnol (Hons) 3/4 Years (Hons) Full-time

ENTRANCE QUALIFICATIONS GCSEs/SCEs required: Chemistry, maths (S grade for SCE's). A levels/Scottish Highers required: two A levels, three Scottish Highers (at least one maths or science subject). A levels/ Scottish Highers preferred: Maths, English, chemistry, biology, geography, environmental science, physics. Scottish Higher grades required: BBC. **Other entry qualifications:** Suitable passes in SCOTVEC HND/BTEC HND courses in relevant subjects may give entry direct to year 3 of the course. Other equivalent qualifications may also be accepted – contact the college to discuss. **Mature applicants:** Experience, maturity and motivation may be accepted in place of formal qualification. **STUDENT NUMBERS Annual applications:** 80–100 (1994). **Annual places:** 26 (1994). **COURSE PROFILE:** Vocational business management degree with an understudy of science and technology. There are two industrial placements at the ends of years 1 and 2 in the UK or Europe. Jointly taught by SAC and the University of Aberdeen. There are seven degree programmes after a core first year students have choice of subjects. **FUTURE DEVELOPMENTS:** Have three new European programmes which include students studying a language in their first year and carrying out a placement abroad.

SCOTTISH AGRICULTURAL COLLEGE – EDINBURGH
Rural Resources
BSc/BSc (Hons) 3/4 Years Full-time

ENTRANCE QUALIFICATIONS GCSEs/SCEs required: English, chemistry if not offered at a higher level. GCSEs/SCEs preferred: Maths, biology, geography, physics. A levels/Scottish Highers required: two A levels at least one in maths or a science subject, three Scottish Highers two from maths, biology, chemistry, physics, geography. Scottish Higher grades required: CCC. **Other entry qualifications:** BTEC Diploma, SCOTVEC NC in appropriate subjects or any equivalent qualifications. **Mature applicants:** Maturity, experience and motivation may be accepted in place of formal qualifications, individual cases are discussed with the relevant tutor. **STUDENT NUMBERS Annual applications:** 200 (1994). **Annual places:** 30 (1994). **EMPLOYMENT ENTERED:** Urban wildlife manager, European officer, environmental information and training officer, access development officer, project assistant, environmental planner, rural business manager. **COURSE PROFILE:** To provide an appropriate education and training to produce rural resource managers with a thorough understanding of scientific, technical, socio-economic and business principles appropriate for a diversity of management careers in the rural or environmental industries. **FUTURE DEVELOPMENTS:** Revised degree options will be available in 1995. All new options will link with the HND in Rural Resource Management.

SHEFFIELD HALLAM UNIVERSITY
Environmental Management
BSc (Hons) 4 Years Sandwich

ENTRANCE QUALIFICATIONS GCSEs/SCEs required: five passes of which two must be at A grade and include English, maths and a science. GCSEs/SCEs preferred: Science, geography. A levels/Scottish Highers required: A science subject. A levels/Scottish Highers preferred: Chemistry, physics, biology. **Other entry qualifications:** BTEC ND/NC with three Merit passes or equivalent qualifications. **Mature applicants:** Considered on motivation, experience, academic attainments and ability. **STUDENT NUMBERS Annual applications:** 344 (1994). **Annual places:** 40 (1994). **EMPLOYMENT ENTERED:** Local authorities, education, manufacturing industries, water related industries, environmental consultants, government departments. **COURSE PROFILE:** Environmental science and engineering, quality monitoring, landscape management, public health planning, impact assessment, management including finance and law. Final year options – natural/urban/industrial/water environment. **FUTURE DEVELOPMENTS:** The course is delivered on restructured semester basis, consideration is being given to additional optional (specialist) units in the final year.

UNIVERSITY OF SHEFFIELD
Natural Environmental Science
BSc 3 Years Full-time

SOUTHAMPTON INSTITUTE
Maritime Environmental Science
BSc (Hons) 3 Years Full-time

ENTRANCE QUALIFICATIONS GCSEs/SCEs preferred: Maths, science. A levels/Scottish Highers required: two A levels or four AS levels to include science based subjects studied to A level. A level/Scottish Highers preferred: Biology, chemistry, physics, maths. **Other entry qualifications:** BTEC ND/NC. **Mature applicants:** A satisfactory general standard of education and appropriate experience. **STUDENT NUMBERS Annual applications:** 40 (1994). **Annual places:** 25 (1994). **EMPLOYMENT ENTERED:** Ecology and environmental management, is a vibrant employment sector, with graduates working in the government sector, environmental consultancy and many non-governmental organisations. **COURSE PROFILE:** Graduates will have developed analytical skills and have a broad understanding of marine environmental issues. Particular emphasis is placed on practical work and field work. **FUTURE DEVELOPMENTS:** This is a new degree course and small changes are constantly being made in response to current issues. We hope to develop student exchanges with the US.

SOUTHAMPTON INSTITUTE
Maritime Environmental Management
BSc (Hons) 3 Years Full-time

ENTRANCE QUALIFICATIONS GCSEs/SCEs required: three at grade C preferably English, maths and any science. A levels/Scottish Highers required: two A levels or four AS levels. A level/Scottish Higher grades preferred: Geography, environmental science, biology, business studies. **Other entry qualifications:** BTEC ND/NC with minimum of three Merit passes (GNVQ equivalent). **Mature applicants:** Considered on individual merit, satisfactory standard of education and experience. **STUDENT NUMBERS Annual applications:** 100 (1994). **Annual places:** 48 (1994). **COURSE PROFILE:** This course is unique in that it specialises in maritime and environmental issues. The course has an over-riding emphasis on sustainable development of the coast, in-shore waters and the ocean. Pathways in resource management, environmental policy, leisure and the environment and hydrographic surveying.

UNIVERSITY OF SOUTHAMPTON
Environmental Engineering
BEng 3 Years Full-time

ENTRANCE QUALIFICATIONS A levels/Scottish Highers required: Maths, a science + one other. A level/Scottish Higher grades required: B (maths) + B (science), BCC (others). **Other entry qualifications:** Physics preferred, ND, Baccalaureate. **Mature applicants:** Welcome. **STUDENT NUMBERS Annual applications:** 93 (1994). **Annual places:** 25 (1994). **COURSE PROFILE:** The course trains engineers to have an enhanced understanding of the environmental aspects of civil engineering development, equipped with new skills to meet these challenges. It is accredited by the Institution of Civil Engineers and IWEM.

UNIVERSITY OF SOUTHAMPTON
Environmental Sciences
BSc (Hons) 3 Years Full or Part-time

ENTRANCE QUALIFICATIONS GCSEs/SCEs required: Maths, chemistry (or dual award science). A levels/Scottish Highers required: preferred three A-levels (or equivalent, two of which must be in science subjects. A level/Scottish Higher grades required: BBBBB. **Other entry qualifications:** OND, ONC, AS, Baccalaureate. **Mature applicants:** Welcome and considered on an individual basis. **STUDENT NUMBERS Annual applications:** 450 (1994). **Annual places:** 40 (1994). **COURSE PROFILE:** A broad modular course drawing from courses in specialist departments including: biology, geography, geology, oceanography, chemistry, law and civil engineering. Students register for a coherent study 'pathway' chosen from human, biological, chemical, physical, scientific management or water environment.

SOUTH BANK UNIVERSITY
Environmental Biology with Management
BSc (Hons) 3 Years Full-time or 4 Years Sandwich

ENTRANCE QUALIFICATIONS GCSEs/SCEs required: five including maths and English. A levels/Scottish Highers required: one science. A level/Scottish Higher grades required: CCCC. **Other entry qualifications:** AS, BTEC, GNVQ (National and Advanced). **Mature applicants:** Welcome and considered on merit. **STUDENT NUMBERS Annual applications:** 180 (1994). **Annual places:** 40 (1994). **COURSE PROFILE:** Aims to provide an understanding of ecological systems, an appreciation of their complexity and an ability to use the various technologies that help to limit environmental damage. There is also a management route within the course which adds a commercial and human resource dimension.

SOUTH BANK UNIVERSITY
Environmental Policy and Environmental Science
BSc 3 Years Full-time

ENTRANCE QUALIFICATIONS GCSEs/SCEs required: Maths. A levels/ Scottish Highers required: A science subject. A level/Scottish Higher grades required: CCCC. **Other entry qualifications:** BTEC National, AS, Advanced GNVQ. **Mature applicants:** Welcome and considered on merit. **STUDENT NUMBERS Annual applications:** 50 (1994). **Annual places:** 30 (1994). **COURSE PROFILE:** Seeks to develop the necessary skills to formulate, evaluate and implement environmental policy in rural management, housing, land policy, ecology etc. There is also a comprehensive review of the ecological and biological aspects of the environment.

SOUTH BANK UNIVERSITY
Environmental Policy and Human Geography
BA or BSc 3 Years Full-time

ENTRANCE QUALIFICATIONS GCSEs/SCEs required: Maths. A levels/ Scottish Highers required: A science subject. A level/Scottish Higher grades required: CCCC. **Other entry qualifications:** BTEC National, AS, Advanced GNVQ. **Mature applicants:** Welcome and considered on merit. **STUDENT NUMBERS Annual applications:** 100 (1994). **Annual places:** 50 (1994). **COURSE PROFILE:** The course progresses from a broad theoretical base to a more global perspective. Study areas include policy evaluation and implementation, race, policy and the environment.

UNIVERSITY OF STIRLING
Conservation Management
BSc 4 Years with placement Full-time or 5 Years Part-time

ENTRANCE QUALIFICATIONS GCSEs/SCEs required: Maths and science (eg biology, chemistry, physics, geography). A levels/Scottish Highers preferred: Geography, biology. A level/Scottish Higher grades required:

BBCC. **Other entry qualifications:** A Level BC or CCC in sciences. **Mature applicants:** Encouraged to apply. References and relevant experience required. **STUDENT NUMBERS Annual applications:** 60 (1994). **Annual places:** 20 (1994). **COURSE PROFILE:** The degree course provides students with an opportunity to understand and contribute to the conservation and management of environmental systems. Agency based placements in conservation work. **FUTURE DEVELOPMENTS:** Introduction of sustainable development option (4th year).

UNIVERSITY OF STIRLING
Environmental Science
BSc 4 Years Full or Part-time

ENTRANCE QUALIFICATIONS GCSEs/SCEs required: Maths. A levels/ Scottish Highers preferred: Geography, biology, chemistry, physics, maths. A level/Scottish Higher grades required: BBCC. **Other entry qualifications:** A level BC or CCC in science subjects. European and North American visitors considered. **Mature applicants:** Encouraged to apply. References and relevant experience required. **STUDENT NUMBERS Annual applications:** 400 (1994). **Annual places:** 70 (1994). **COURSE PROFILE:** A primary area of the BSc degree is to promote an understanding of the functioning of near surface bio-physical systems and the complex interaction between them. Emphasis on science and the human influence on natural systems and the management of these systems. **FUTURE DEVELOPMENTS:** Sustainable development 4th year option.

SUFFOLK COLLEGE
Environmental Studies
BSc 3 Years Full or Part-time

ENTRANCE QUALIFICATIONS GCSEs/SCEs required: four including maths, English and a science. A levels/Scottish Highers required: two including a science. **Other entry qualifications:** ONC, OND, GNVQ Advanced, Access, APEL. **Mature applicants:** Contact direct. **STUDENT NUMBERS Annual applications:** 20 (1994). **Annual places:** 16 (1994). **COURSE PROFILE:** This modular environmental studies course investigates the natural environment, its patterns and processes and the human impact on it. It provides the knowledge and skills necessary for an informed understanding of the environment, its problems and their solutions. **FUTURE DEVELOPMENTS:** Developing an MSc in Environmental Management for start of academic year 1995/6. Course can be studied as a joint route with IT or Business Studies.

UNIVERSITY OF SUNDERLAND
Environmental Technology
BSc 3 Years Full-time or 4 Years Sandwich

ENTRANCE QUALIFICATIONS GCSEs/SCEs required: three maths, English, science preferred. A levels/Scottish Highers required: two including a science. A level/Scottish Higher grades required: Cs. **Other entry qualifications:** All considered. **Mature applicants:** By interview. **STUDENT NUMBERS Annual applications:** 280 (1994). **Annual places:** 90 (1994). **COURSE PROFILE:** Enables environmental problems to be assessed and solved. Includes management based modules as well as a core of environmental technology and managerial skills and produces graduates who see their roles as being active in decision-making and the promotion of environmental enterprises.

UNIVERSITY OF SUNDERLAND
Environmental Studies
BSc 3 Years Full-time or 4 Years Part-time/Sandwich

ENTRANCE QUALIFICATIONS GCSEs/SCEs required: three including maths. A levels/Scottish Highers required: two. A level/Scottish Higher grades required: CCCCC. **Other entry qualifications:** All considered. University entrance requirements required. **Mature applicants:** Welcome. Entry requirements flexible. **STUDENT NUMBERS Annual places:** 120 (1994). **COURSE PROFILE:** Initially a common interdisciplinary foundation curriculum. Opportunities to specialise in fields including: pollution and waste management, environment, business and development; wildlife and countryside management; energy policy; urban management. Integrative units on environmental techniques, management decision taking, issues and policies, education and information underpin the programme of options. **FUTURE DEVELOPMENTS:** Course continually improved and updated. Specialist pollution analysis module expected to operate in 1995.

UNIVERSITY OF SUNDERLAND
Environmental Geology
BSc (Hons) 3 Years Full-time or 4 Years Sandwich

ENTRANCE QUALIFICATIONS GCSEs/SCEs required: Maths, English. Physics preferred. A levels/Scottish Highers required: two (10pts), one science subject. A level/Scottish Higher grades required: CCC. **Other entry qualifications:** two AS's per A Level, GNVQ science + A Level, OND/ONC considered. **Mature applicants:** Each applicant considered individually, evidence of recent learning success required. **STUDENT NUMBERS Annual applications:** 76 (1994). **Annual places:** 18 (1994).

COURSE PROFILE: Core modules in traditional geology with specialist modules (levels 2 and 3) in hydrology, environmental geochemistry, resources, engineering geology etc. Preparation for the role of a professional environmental geologist which includes a study of aspects of environmental legislation and environmental impact assessments.

UNIVERSITY OF SUNDERLAND
Energy Technology Management
BSc 3 Years Full-time or 4 Years Sandwich

ENTRANCE QUALIFICATIONS GCSEs/SCEs required: Maths, English. chemistry. A levels/Scottish Highers preferred: Economics, maths, physics, chemistry, French/German. **Other entry qualifications:** All considered. **Mature applicants:** Each considered on an individual basis, interview normally required. **STUDENT NUMBERS Annual applications:** 32 (1994). **Annual places:** 15 (1994). **COURSE PROFILE:** After introducing major issues in year 1, subjects such as energy resources, technologies, technoeconomics, information analysis and modelling are developed in year 2. After industrial placement in year 3, energy modelling, conservation, economics and environmental impact are extensively studies in the final year. **FUTURE DEVELOPMENTS:** For 1995/96 a wider choice of modules are being made available ie i) Air and Water Pollution ii) Environmental Engineering. Speakers from industry are being contacted. Course validation by IES is being sought.

ST MARY'S COLLEGE (UNIVERSITY OF SURREY)
Environmental Science
BSc 3 Years (4 Years with 1 year placement) Full-time

ENTRANCE QUALIFICATIONS GCSEs/SCEs preferred: Those subjects in science not offered at A level, chemistry, biology, geography, maths. A levels/Scottish Highers required: two A levels or equivalent of which at least one must be; chemistry, biology, geography, geology, physics or maths. A level/Scottish Higher grades required: At least 8 points, five Scottish Highers with at least three at higher grade in science. **Other entry qualifications:** Details from registry. **Mature applicants:** We look for commitment and enthusiasm for the course and preferably some experience of working in the environmental field. Some evidence that science has been studies expected. **STUDENT NUMBERS Annual applications:** 120 (1994). **Annual places:** 35 (1994). **COURSE PROFILE:** Course designed to give students broad based knowledge and proficiency in a range of environmental sciences in first two years, allowing for specialisation in final year, including research project option. Industrial placement an additional year.

FUTURE DEVELOPMENTS: New module on 'legal aspects of environmental control' has been added since 1993 in final year.

UNIVERSITY OF SUSSEX
Ecology and Conservation
BSc 3 Years Full-time

ENTRANCE QUALIFICATIONS GCSEs/SCEs required: Chemistry, maths, English. A levels/Scottish Highers required: one science. A level/Scottish Higher grades required: BCD. **Other entry qualifications:** Access. All considered on an equivalency basis. **Mature applicants:** Welcome. Flexible entrance requirements. **STUDENT NUMBERS Annual applications:** 250 (1994). **Annual places:** 25 (1994). **COURSE PROFILE:** A broad first year includes evolution, physiology, biochemistry and environmental chemistry. A more specialised second year covers biogeography, methods in ecology and conservation, systematics, genetics for ecologists, introduction to conservation and others. A research project and a wide range of options comprise the third year.

UNIVERSITY OF SUSSEX
Environmental Science
BSc 3 Years Full-time

TRINITY COLLEGE – CARMARTHEN
The Rural Environment
BSc (Hons) 3 Years Full-time

ENTRANCE QUALIFICATIONS GCSEs/SCEs preferred: Biology, geography, maths, science. A levels/Scottish Highers preferred: Biology, geography, environmental studies/science, computing. **Other entry qualifications:** A level equivalent. **Mature applicants:** Interview. **STUDENT NUMBERS Annual applications:** 109 (1994). **Annual places:** 36 (1994). **COURSE PROFILE:** This is an integrated degree which encompasses the following broad areas: The structure and functioning of rural environments; the management of that environment for conservation and socio-economic development.

TRINITY COLLEGE – CARMARTHEN
Heritage Conservation
BSc 3 Years Full-time

ENTRANCE QUALIFICATIONS GCSEs/SCEs preferred: Chemistry, biology, physics, geology, geography, history, archaeology. A levels/Scottish Highers preferred: Archaeology, geology, geography, history, any science.

Other entry qualifications: International Baccalaureate and appropriate European qualifications accepted. **Mature applicants:** Considered on merit – need not necessarily have A level or equivalent. **STUDENT NUMBERS Annual applications:** 14 (1994). **Annual places:** 14 (1994). **COURSE PROFILE:** The course covers four inter-related areas of study: management and information technology, archaeology, environmental and materials science, and heritage conservation. The course also includes six weeks archaeological fieldwork experience and six weeks management placement.

TRINITY COLLEGE – CARMARTHEN
Health and the Environment
BSc (Hons) 3 Years Full-time

ENTRANCE QUALIFICATIONS GCSEs/SCEs required: Biology/Science. Chemistry, maths preferred. A levels/Scottish Highers preferred: Biology, chemistry. **Other entry qualifications:** A level equivalent. **Mature applicants:** By interview. **STUDENT NUMBERS Annual applications:** 18 (1994). **Annual places:** 12 (1994). **COURSE PROFILE:** This is an integrated degree course concerned with human impact on the environment and the effect of the environment of human health and ecosystems.

UNIVERSITY OF ULSTER
Environmental Science
BSc/BSc (Hons) 3 Years Full-time or 4 Years Sandwich

ENTRANCE QUALIFICATIONS GCSEs/SCEs required: Maths. Modern language required for four year course. Biology, geography, physics and chemistry preferred. A levels/Scottish Highers required: two or more approved sciences at A or AS level. Science subjects preferred for Hons courses. A level/Scottish Higher grades required: BBB+1 for Hons. BCCC for degree course. **Mature applicants:** Must be 21 years of age at date of entry, have useful experience to bring to University studies, realistic chance of completing course. May be asked to take test. **STUDENT NUMBERS Annual applications:** 583 (1994). **Annual places:** 45 (1994). **COURSE PROFILE:** The course is highly interdisciplinary, embracing ecology, geography, meteorology, hydrology, geology, pedology, information technology and its applications, environmental alternatives and management of the environment. **FUTURE DEVELOPMENTS:** An additional strand after year 1 to include quality analysis and modelling in such areas as water and air pollution management and control.

UNIVERSITY COLLEGE OF WALES – ABERYSTWYTH
Environmental Science
BSc 3 Years Full-time

ENTRANCE QUALIFICATIONS GCSEs/SCEs required: Maths, English, chemistry. A levels/Scottish Highers preferred: Biology, chemistry, geography. A level/Scottish Higher grades required: BBBCC. **Other entry qualifications:** All considered on merit. **Mature applicants:** Warmly welcomed. **STUDENT NUMBERS Annual applications:** 200 (1994). Annual places: 35 (1994). **COURSE PROFILE:** Biological sciences and earth studies deliver this Honours course. Its remit is to train graduates for work in the environmental field and to provide them with skills in earth studies and biology, together with an insight into the life of plants, animals and micro-organisms. **FUTURE DEVELOPMENTS:** Under review for 1996. Possible changes in modular organisation.

UNIVERSITY OF WALES – BANGOR
Environmental Biology
BSc 3 Years Full-time

ENTRANCE QUALIFICATIONS GCSEs/SCEs required: Maths. Chemistry, biology or combined sciences preferred. A levels/Scottish Highers required: two sciences. Biology, chemistry preferred. A level/Scottish Higher grades required: BBBB. **Other entry qualifications:** Baccalaureate, AS chemistry. **Mature applicants:** BTEC or Access course, plus a formal interview. **STUDENT NUMBERS Annual applications:** 250 (1994). **Annual places:** 25 (1994). **COURSE PROFILE:** Environmental biology at Bangor focuses on the diversity of life on our planet, the complexity of environments, and inter-relationships between the two. Bangor is ideally located for this course, allowing ready access to the Snowdonia National Park, marine and freshwater ecosystems etc.

UNIVERSITY OF WALES – BANGOR
Rural Resource Management
BSc 3 Years Full-time

ENTRANCE QUALIFICATIONS GCSEs/SCEs required: English/Welsh, maths. GCSE/SCE preferred: Biology. A levels/Scottish Highers required: two/three A levels. Five Scottish Highers. Preferred appropriate subjects: biology, geography, economics, maths, physics, chemistry, geology, English. A level/Scottish Higher grades required: BBBC. **Other entry qualifications:** All considered. **Mature applicants:** A levels, Access or Foundation preferred. **STUDENT NUMBERS Annual applications:** 175 (1994). **Annual places:** 20 (1994). **COURSE PROFILE:** This course is designed to allow a degree of specialisation within a common framework of economics and the sciences which have particular relevance in a rural context: agriculture, forestry, biology and ecology. In addition courses which integrate the common rural resource management theme are taught in parallel.

UNIVERSITY OF WALES – BANGOR
Environmental Sciences
BSc 3 Years Full-time

ENTRANCE QUALIFICATIONS GCSEs/SCEs required: English/Welsh. GCSEs/SCEs preferred: Maths and sciences. A levels/Scottish Highers preferred: Biology, maths, physics, chemistry, economics, geology, geography. A level/Scottish Higher grades required: BBBC. **Other entry qualifications:** All considered. **Mature applicants:** A levels, Access or Foundation preferred. **STUDENT NUMBERS Annual applications:** 205 (1994). **Annual places:** 10 (1994). **COURSE PROFILE:** In addition to six or seven core modules in each year, students can specialise in an area of their choice by selecting appropriate modules offered by the many schools within the Faculty of Science.

UNIVERSITY OF WALES – BANGOR
Environmental Chemistry
BSc (Hons) 3 Years Full-time

ENTRANCE QUALIFICATIONS GCSEs/SCEs required: five including English/Welsh. A levels/Scottish Highers required: two including chemistry. A level/Scottish Higher grades required: 12 points generally required. **Other entry qualifications:** All considered. **Mature applicants:** Welcomed. **STUDENT NUMBERS Annual applications:** 50 (1994). **Annual places:** 10 (1994). **COURSE PROFILE:** A degree which provides a basic training in chemistry, with particular relevance to the chemistry of the environment. A scientific study of the environmental chemistry is concerned with all aspects of the problems of the environment from a knowledge of the basic chemistry involved to an understanding of the nature of the earth, the seas and atmospheric processes. An entry into careers in laboratories dealing with environmental problems (water authorities, local authorities, consultancy firms, industrial companies).

UNIVERSITY OF WALES – CARDIFF
Marine Geography
BSc 3 Years Full-time or 4 Years Sandwich

ENTRANCE QUALIFICATIONS GCSEs/SCEs preferred: Maths. A levels/ Scottish Highers preferred: Geography. A level/Scottish Higher grades required: ABBBC. **Other entry qualifications:** BTEC three Merits, two Distinctions, International Baccalaureate. **Mature applicants:** Acceptable. **STUDENT NUMBERS Annual applications:** 180 (1994). **Annual places:** 40 (1994). **COURSE PROFILE:** Overall theme if development and management of marine coastal regions, with emphasis on transferable skills in the field. Part 1: Basic physical/human geography, natural/social sciences subject. Part 2/3: Specialisation in marine science, marine industrial sectors, integrated coastal/ocean management.

UNIVERSITY OF WALES – CARDIFF
Marine Geography (Marine Resource Management)
BSc 3 Years Full-time or 4 Years Sandwich

ENTRANCE QUALIFICATIONS GCSEs/SCEs preferred: Maths. A levels/ Scottish Highers preferred: Geography. A level/Scottish Higher grades required: ABBBC. **Other entry qualifications:** BTEC three Merits, two Distinctions, International Baccalaureate. **Mature applicants:** Acceptable. **STUDENT NUMBERS Annual applications:** 180 (1994). **Annual places:** 10 (1994). **COURSE PROFILE:** Overall theme of development and management of marine and coastal regions, with emphasis on transferable skills in the field. Part 1: Basic physical/human geography, natural/social sciences. Part 2/3: Specialisation in marine sciences, marine industrial sectors, integrated coastal/ocean management, environmental evaluation and law and economics.

UNIVERSITY OF WALES – CARDIFF
Environmental Engineering
BEng 3 Years Full-time

ENTRANCE QUALIFICATIONS GCSEs/SCEs preferred: Chemistry. A levels/Scottish Highers required: Maths. A level/Scottish Higher preferred: Physics. A level/Scottish Higher grades required: CCC. **Other entry qualifications:** two AS considered as one A Level (not maths), BTEC (one Distinction and four Merits at level 3), GNVQ (18 points level 3). **Mature applicants:** Encouraged – each considered on merit. **STUDENT NUMBERS Annual applications:** 100 (1994). Annual places: 15 (1994). **COURSE PROFILE:** Engineering forms the central core, with part 1 being largely common with the other engineering degree schemes. Specialist environmental subjects are introduced in part 1 and expanded in later years. Legislation, Health & Safety and Pollution Control are amongst the specialist subjects. **FUTURE DEVELOPMENTS:** Enhancement of language teaching and offer of one year in Europe (France or Spain).

UNIVERSITY OF WALES – CARDIFF
Environmental Geoscience
BSc 3 Years Full-time

ENTRANCE QUALIFICATIONS A levels/Scottish Highers required: A science or geography. A levels/Scottish Highers preferred: Two additional sciences, arts or language. A level/Scottish Higher grades required: BBBCC. **Other entry qualifications:** All acceptable at suitable levels and attainments. **COURSE PROFILE:** An earth sciences course which includes specialist vocational training in geo-environmental hazards, impact assessment and pollution control, and global environmental change, with choice of other relevant earth sciences modules.

UNIVERSITY OF WALES – CARDIFF
Ecology and Environmental Management
BSc 3 Years Full-time or 4 Years Sandwich

ENTRANCE QUALIFICATIONS GCSEs/SCEs required: English, maths. GCSEs/SCEs preferred: Biology, chemistry or combined sciences. A levels/Scottish Highers preferred: Biology, chemistry. A level/Scottish Higher grades required: BBBB. **Other entry qualifications:** OND, ONC,

AS, Baccalaureate (International and European). **Mature applicants:** With sufficient background to be able to cope with the course. **STUDENT NUMBERS Annual applications:** 170 (1994). **Annual places:** 25 (1994). **COURSE PROFILE:** Evolution and diversity of life on earth, and its conservation. Population and community ecology. Environmental pollution, especially its effects on natural habitats. Land use and conservation ecology.

WEST SUSSEX (CHICESTER) INSTITUTE OF HIGHER EDUCATION
Environmental Science
BA 3 Years Full or Part-time

ENTRANCE QUALIFICATIONS GCSEs/SCEs required: two sciences (or one science and geography). A levels/Scottish Highers preferred: A science and/or geography. **Other entry qualifications:** All considered. **Mature applicants:** Mature Entrants test. **STUDENT NUMBERS Annual applications:** New course for 1995. **COURSE PROFILE:** Environmental science is taken as half a modular degree. Geography is the most likely complementing half. Topics covered include ecology, earth science, atmospheric science, astronomy, energy resources and coastal studies. One module is a field course.

WRITTLE COLLEGE – CHELMSFORD
Rural Resource Development
BSc (Hons) 3 Years Full or Part-time

ENTRANCE QUALIFICATIONS GCSEs/SCEs preferred: Maths and/or sciences. A level/Scottish Higher grades required: C. **Other entry qualifications:** All considered on merit. **Mature applicants:** Welcomed, usually via Access courses. **STUDENT NUMBERS Annual applications:** 200 (1994). **Annual places:** 50 (1994). **COURSE PROFILE:** Common first year prior to choice of five specialist routes. About 40% of second and third years are available to support individual student's choice – along with a core of legal and business studies. Language and European studies options. **FUTURE DEVELOPMENTS:** Increased student choice for 1995 entry. Also stronger support to specialist areas of study.

UNIVERSITY OF YORK
Environmental Economics and Environmental Management
BSc 3 Years Full-time

ENTRANCE QUALIFICATIONS GCSEs/SCEs required: Maths. A levels/ Scottish Highers required: One science or maths, biology, economics and maths preferred subjects. **Other entry qualifications:** All A level equivalent qualifications welcomed. **Mature applicants:** Access welcomed. Mature students encouraged to apply with other qualifications. **STUDENT NUMBERS Annual applications**: 90 (1994). **Annual places:** 26 (1994). **COURSE PROFILE:** The course includes teaching in three departments: Biology, Economics and EEEM. The EEEM courses emphasise the integration of natural science principles with economics in the management of the environment and sustained development. Global issues are emphasised.

Study the Environment at Imperial College

Imperial College offers a unique choice of Undergraduate and Postgraduate courses that cover aspects of environmental science and technology. Courses are available in a variety of disciplines, but all have in common a highly practical approach that will equip you to design, develop and manage solutions to a wide range of environmental problems. As an environmental science and technology graduate, career opportunities exist for you in a variety of fields including government, industry, academia and consultancy.

Undergraduate Courses

Civil and Environmental Engineering (4 year MEng)

Ecology (3 year BSc)

Environmental and Earth Resources Engineering (4 year MEng)

Geology with Environmental Applications (3 year BSc)

Postgraduate Courses (MSc)

Environmental Analysis and Assessment

Environmental Engineering

Environmental Geology

Environmental Technology with Specialist Options in Ecological Management, Energy Policy, Environmental Analysis & Assessment, Water Management, Pollution & Business & the Environment

Hydrology for Environmental Management

Soil Mechanics and Environmental Geotechnics

Courses with environmental modules

A range of Undergraduate and Postgraduate courses are also available in subjects including Biology, Geology, Mechanical Engineering and Management Studies with environmental and environment-related modules/options. Opportunities exist within a number of Departments and Centres for research into environmental issues leading to a PhD.

For Undergraduate and Postgraduate prospectuses write to: The Admissions Office, Registry Division, Imperial College, London SW7 2AZ.

POSTGRADUATE TAUGHT COURSES

ABERDEEN UNIVERSITY
Ecology
MSc/Diploma 1 year Full-time

ENTRANCE QUALIFICATIONS: Degree in relevant science. Grade: 2.2 or above. **Other Selection Criteria:** Interview, experience in conservation work. **STUDENT NUMBERS: Annual Applications:** c.100 (1994). Annual Places: 13 (1994). **EMPLOYMENT ENTERED:** Conservation, monitoring, research institutes (eg Scottish National Heritage, English Nature, NERPB, NRA, universities). **COURSE PROFILE:** The course provides theoretical, practical and technical training, in both plant and animal ecology, at postgraduate level. Various options can be selected in plant, animal and soil science.

UNIVERSITY OF ABERDEEN
Environmental Remote Sensing
MSc 12 or 24 months, Diploma 9 or 20 months, Full- or Part-time

ENTRANCE QUALIFICATIONS: Honours degree for MSc, ordinary/pass degree for diploma. Grade: 2.2 or above for MSc. **Other Selection Criteria:** Two academic references, CVs and occasionally interviews. **STUDENT NUMBERS: Annual Applications:** 35 (1994). **Annual Places:** 14 (1994). **EMPLOYMENT ENTERED:** Environmental consultancy, government departments and agencies (national and local), higher education (research and teaching), NRA, Scottish National Heritage, ODA, Irish Geological Survey, EOSAT. **COURSE PROFILE:** The course covers the theoretical basis and application of techniques for sensing, recording, analysing and displaying the effects of the interaction of electro-magnetic radiation with the earth's surface features. Emphasis is on the use of aircraft and satellite data for environmental mapping and monitoring. **FUTURE DEVELOPMENTS:** From 1995/6 the structure will integrate the remote sensing/GIS technology in a framework of environmental management, monitoring and modelling.

UNIVERSITY OF ABERDEEN
Environmental Science
MSc 1 year Full-time

ENTRANCE QUALIFICATIONS: Undergraduate degree. Grade: Good honours grade or equivalent. **Other Selection Criteria:** Interview for special

scholarships. **STUDENT NUMBERS: Annual Applications:** 157 (1994).
Annual Places: 12 (1994). **EMPLOYMENT ENTERED:** Environmental
consultancy, conservation, pollution control (government and industry),
soil capability and conservation (eg ADAS), forestry and agriculture,
environmental education, environmental impact assessment. **COURSE
PROFILE:** A modular course including: EIA; pollution control; soil
conservation; ecosystem conservation; forestry and agriculture; tropical
ecology; and ecological concepts.

UNIVERSITY OF ABERDEEN (& ROBERT GORDON UNIVERSITY)
Rural & Regional Resources Planning
MSc/Diploma 1 or 2 years Full- or Part-time

ENTRANCE QUALIFICATIONS: Undergraduate degree in appropriate
subject and/or practical experience. Grade: 2.2 or above. **Other Selection
Criteria:** Ability to demonstrate motivation, interest and commitment.
STUDENT NUMBERS: Annual Applications: 130 (1994). **Annual Places:**
c.30 (1994). **EMPLOYMENT ENTERED:** Environmental consultancy,
local government (eg planning), research, international agencies (EU,
World Bank), statutory agencies (Scottish National Heritage, English
Nature), conservation organisations (RSPB). **COURSE PROFILE:** The
course aims to provide specialist training in resource and environmental
management planning, in a rural context. It focuses on the concept and
practise of sustainable development. Students are able to develop their own
interests within the framework of the course.

UNIVERSITY OF BATH
Environmental Science Policy & Planning
MSc/Diploma MSc 1 or 2 Full- or Part-time Diploma 6 months Full-time

ENTRANCE QUALIFICATIONS: Degree in a science, social science or
technology subject. Grade: 2.2 or above. **Other Selection Criteria:** Entrance
qualifications relaxed if candidate has considerable experience in environmental science, policy and/or planning. **STUDENT NUMBERS: Annual Applications:** 82 (1994). **Annual Places:** 24 (1994). **EMPLOYMENT
ENTERED:** Environmental consultancies, government and education.
COURSE PROFILE: Environmental issues are examined from many different perspectives: social, political, economic, scientific and technological.

THE UNIVERSITY OF BIRMINGHAM
Environmental Engineering
MSc 15 months Full-time

ENTRANCE QUALIFICATIONS: Undergraduate engineering or science
degree. **STUDENT NUMBERS: Annual Applications:** New course. **Annual**

Places: 5 (1994). **COURSE PROFILE:** A new taught course/project masters degree concerned with control of emissions from industry.

THE UNIVERSITY OF BIRMINGHAM
International Highway Engineering
MSc(Eng)/Diploma MSc(Eng.) 1 year Full-time Dip. 8 months Full-time (Part-time option for UK/EU students)
ENTRANCE QUALIFICATIONS: Undergraduate degree, three years relevant experience, TOEFL/IELTS 'test of English' score above 500 for overseas applicants. Grade: Good honours degree. **Other Selection Criteria:** Ability to fund your place, interviews for UK applicants. **STUDENT NUMBERS: Annual Applications:** 120 (1994). **Annual Places:** 29 (1994). **EMPLOYMENT ENTERED:** High/middle management in public/private sector highway/traffic engineering establishments. The diploma is suitable for non-engineers who wish to, or who are already, working in the highways sector. **COURSE PROFILE:** The course covers: highway economics; financing and budgeting; traffic planning and environmental issues; traffic engineering and management; traffic safety; geotechnical engineering; construction aggregates and bituminous materials; highway design; highway drainage; construction; pavement design and management; maintenance; numerical methods; operations research. **FUTURE DEVELOPMENTS:** Plan to increase the relevant environmental content.

THE UNIVERSITY OF BIRMINGHAM
Water Resources Technology and Management
MSc(Eng) 1 year Full-time
ENTRANCE QUALIFICATIONS: Honours degree in engineering. Grade: 2.2 or above. **Other Selection Criteria:** Interviews where possible. **STUDENT NUMBERS: Annual Applications:** 152 (1994). **Annual Places:** 39 (1994). **EMPLOYMENT ENTERED:** Civil engineering, environmental consultants, NRA, water companies, research organisations. **COURSE PROFILE:** The course includes: water quality management; water and wastewater treatment; surface and groundwater resource assessment and development; river engineering and management; environmental impact assessment; irrigation scheme design and operation; water distribution and sewerage systems; management techniques and project appraisal; computer design and management software; information technology.

BOLTON INSTITUTE OF HIGHER EDUCATION
Geotechnical Engineering
MSc 1 year Full-time 3 years Part-time
ENTRANCE QUALIFICATIONS: Undergraduate degree in civil engineering, geology, geography, or related subject. Grade: 2.2. **Other Selection**

Criteria: Mature candidates and persons wishing to change career directions are given separate considerations. **STUDENT NUMBERS: Annual Applications:** 21 (1994). **Annual Places:** 15 (1994). **EMPLOYMENT ENTERED:** Ground engineering, waste disposal, environmental consultancy, insurance. **COURSE PROFILE:** The direction of the course is engineering associated with the ground and corresponding environmental interactions/constraints/considerations. The course is directed towards problem solving and positive, completed action. **FUTURE DEVELOPMENTS:** Additional environmental modules to be created.

BOURNEMOUTH UNIVERSITY
Coastal Zone Management
MSc/Postgraduate Diploma 50 weeks Full-time

ENTRANCE QUALIFICATIONS: Undergraduate degree, HND considered with evidence of relevant work experience. Grade: 2.1 preferred, 2.2 considered. **Other Selection Criteria:** Interview, relevant work experience. **STUDENT NUMBERS: Annual Applications:** 60 (1994). **Annual Places:** 22 (1994). **EMPLOYMENT ENTERED:** Consultancy, regulatory bodies, local authorities. **COURSE PROFILE:** A full-time programme running for 50 weeks, 12 taught units in two semesters: Coastal Zone Management; Marine Resource Management; Coastal Law; Marine Pollution; Environmental Information Systems; Ecological and Environmental Management; Marine Heritage Science; Leisure and the Coastal Zone; Project Planning. Ten week practical placement and ten week dissertation.

BOURNEMOUTH UNIVERSITY
Water Environments
MSc 1 year Full-time

ENTRANCE QUALIFICATIONS: Undergraduate degree or, in some circumstances, HND or APL. **Other Selection Criteria:** Interviews and students selected to bring a mix of disciplines and experience to the course. **STUDENT NUMBERS: Annual Applications:** Approx. 300. **Annual Places:** 50 (1994). **EMPLOYMENT ENTERED:** Economic regulation (eg OFWAT), environmental regulation (eg NRA), water utilities (eg Wessex Water), environmental consultants, engineering consultants, waste management, trade associations, research bodies, remote imaging. **COURSE PROFILE:** The course is designed to develop managers able to operate effectively in the multidisciplinary environment of the modern water sector. Emphasis is placed initially on developing transferable skills, the three modules provide a firm technological base for the four taught modules concentrating on management topics. Students then undertake a six month placement, during which the research dissertation is prepared, in which the 'real world' emphasis of the entire course is practised so as to provide an identifiable and useable item of work. **FUTURE DEVELOPMENTS:** A course for overseas students, a part-time route and new strands based on the core components are being considered.

UNIVERSITY OF BRADFORD
Business Strategy & Environmental Management
MSc/Postgraduate Diploma 1 year Full-time 2/3 years Part-time

ENTRANCE QUALIFICATIONS: Undergraduate degree in a related subject. Grade: 2.1 or above. **Other Selection Criteria:** Two years environmental or managerial experience preferred and candidates without formal qualifications but with considerable relevant experience are welcome to apply. **STUDENT NUMBERS: Annual Applications:** 40 (1994). **Annual Places:** 15 (1994). **EMPLOYMENT ENTERED:** New course. **COURSE PROFILE:** The course combines latest developments in environmental management, business strategy and environmental technology. The aim is to equip business managers with environmental knowledge and environmental scientists with appropriate management skills, to enable both to adopt appropriate policies, principles and practises.

UNIVERSITY OF BRADFORD
Environmental Monitoring
MSc 1 year Full-time

ENTRANCE QUALIFICATIONS: Non environmental science BSc (Hons) degree. Grade: 2.2 or above. **Other Selection Criteria:** Application form and interview. **STUDENT NUMBERS: Annual Applications:** 130 (1994). **Annual Places:** 22 (1994). **EMPLOYMENT ENTERED:** South Yorkshire Waste Regulation Authority, Westlakes Research Institute, Severn Trent and Welsh Regions National Rivers Authority. **COURSE PROFILE:** This conversion course comprises practicals, lectures, workshops and seminars on: environmental monitoring; experimental design; biomonitoring; GIS and environmental applications; environmental economics; and management case studies and issues. The three month project allows specialisation in a particular area of environmental monitoring. **FUTURE DEVELOPMENTS:** 1995/96 sessions will include a revised unit on waste management and recycling.

UNIVERSITY OF BRISTOL
Ecology and Management of the Natural Environment
MSc/Diploma 2 years extended study Full-time

ENTRANCE QUALIFICATIONS: Honours degree in a science with an environmental or biological basis. **COURSE PROFILE:** The aim of the course is to prepare participants thoroughly, on a sound ecological and professional basis. Emphasis on field work. There are three taught modular units: Ecological Principles in Management; Practical Ecological Management and Professional Practice in Ecological Management, and one research unit, which must be a piece of original investigation. A diploma course is available for applicants who do not wish to undertake the dissertation unit.

BRUNEL UNIVERSITY
Environmental Science with Legislation and Management
MSc 1 or 2 years Full- or Part-time

ENTRANCE QUALIFICATIONS: Undergraduate degree or equivalent. **STUDENT NUMBERS: Annual Applications:** 50+ Full-time, 15 Part-time (1994). **Annual Places:** 24 Full-time, 13 Part-time (1994). **EMPLOYMENT ENTERED:** Local authority environmental health departments, water authorities, environmental consultancies. **COURSE PROFILE:** A course designed to produce graduates with a strong technical basis, a good working knowledge of UK and EU legislation and appropriate project and environmental management skills. Industrial placements available.

BRUNEL UNIVERSITY
Environmental Pollution Science
MSc 1 or 2 years Full- or Part-time

ENTRANCE QUALIFICATIONS: Undergraduate degree or equivalent. **STUDENT NUMBERS: Annual Applications:** 50+ Full-time, 10 Part-time (1994). **Annual Places:** 19 Full-time, 6 Part-time (1994). **EMPLOYMENT ENTERED:** Local authority environmental health departments, water authorities, environmental consultancies. **COURSE PROFILE:** A course designed to produce graduates with a strong technical understanding of pollution and its control, supported by practical, hands-on problem solving skills. Industrial placements available.

UNIVERSITY OF CENTRAL ENGLAND IN BIRMINGHAM
Environmental Management
MA 1 or 2 years Full- or Part-time

ENTRANCE QUALIFICATIONS: Undergraduate degree and/or professional qualifications. **Other Selection Criteria:** Some experience with an environmental agency is preferable. **STUDENT NUMBERS: Annual Applications:** 25 (1994, Part-time only). **Annual Places:** 15 (1994, Part-time only). **EMPLOYMENT ENTERED:** A wide range of organisations with environmental responsibilities eg local authorities (planning, environmental health), central government bodies (NRA, British Waterways), voluntary bodies (The National Trust, The Groundwork Trust) and private companies (British Telecom, British Gas). **COURSE PROFILE:** The course focuses on environmental policy evaluation and management of environmental control processes. Specialist options are available from a cross-faculty range.

UNIVERSITY OF CENTRAL ENGLAND IN BIRMINGHAM
Environmental Pollution Control
MSc 1 year Full-time or 2 years minimum Part-time (Option to take Postgraduate Diploma/Postgraduate Certificate)

ENTRANCE QUALIFICATIONS: Honours degree in science or engineering. Grade: Good honours. **Other Selection Criteria:** All applicants are interviewed. **STUDENT NUMBERS: Annual Applications:** 100 (1994). **Annual Places:** 20 (1994). **EMPLOYMENT ENTERED:** Local authorities, manufacturing companies, consultancies and government bodies. **COURSE PROFILE:** An integrated, project driven course. There are four blocks of study: pollution science; environmental law; environmental management; resource utilisation. Students undertake a project associated with each block. An industrial project, of 16 weeks duration, forms the basis of the Masters dissertation.

UNIVERSITY OF CENTRAL LANCASHIRE
Environmental Law
LLM/Postgraduate Diploma 1 or 2 years Full- or Part-time

ENTRANCE QUALIFICATIONS: Undergraduate degree in any discipline. Grade: 2.2 honours or above. **Other Selection Criteria:** Interview, appropriate experience in/commitment to the environmental field, other relevant qualifications considered. **STUDENT NUMBERS: Annual Applications:** 40 (1994). **Annual Places:** 15 (1994, on each of the Full- and Part-time courses). **EMPLOYMENT ENTERED:** Primarily law firms, although 1994 was the first year of completion. **COURSE PROFILE:** The course is interdisciplinary and aims to provide an in depth knowledge of UK, European and international law, plus lawyers skills for non-lawyers. It is recognised that the law cannot operate in a vacuum, non-law modules include Chemistry of the Environment and Research Methods with optional units in, Environmental Toxicology and Environmental Policy.

CHESTER COLLEGE OF HIGHER EDUCATION
Environmental Biology
MSc/Diploma 1-2 years Full- or Part-time

ENTRANCE QUALIFICATIONS: Undergraduate degree, suitable environmental/industrial experience. Grade: 2.2 honours or above. **Other Selection Criteria:** Interviews and references. **STUDENT NUMBERS: Annual Applications:** 55 (1994). **Annual Places:** 44 (1994). **EMPLOYMENT ENTERED:** Ecotoxicology (Unilever, Atomic Energy Authority, Shell), environment (English Heritage, local authorities), environmental health and ecology. **COURSE PROFILE:** Areas covered include: environmental pollution; ecotoxicology; ecology; conservation and management of the environment. Students need to be able to demonstrate 'practical ability' in their research dissertations. Industrial placements available. **FUTURE DEVELOPMENTS:** Plans to open the course up for distance learning.

COVENTRY UNIVERSITY
Environmental Monitoring and Assessment
MSc/Postgraduate Diploma 1 year Full-time 2-3 years Part-time

ENTRANCE QUALIFICATIONS: Undergraduate degree. Grade: Good honours. **Other Selection Criteria:** References essential, interviews for non-standard entry. **STUDENT NUMBERS: Annual Applications:** 100 (1994). **Annual Places:** 15 (1994). **EMPLOYMENT ENTERED:** Consultancy companies, regulatory authorities (local authorities, NRA), water companies, government agencies and industry. **COURSE PROFILE:** The course contains compulsory units in Environmental Law and International Environmental Law. Options include: Environmental Monitoring; Environmental Auditing; Environmental Management; Water Pollution; Air Pollution; Waste Management; Contaminated Land. The course is vocational and industrially based with an excellent employment record. **FUTURE DEVELOPMENTS:** New modules in Noise and GIS.

CRANFIELD UNIVERSITY
Applied Energy Studies
MSc/Diploma 2 years (1st year at UTC, Compiegne, France, 2nd year at Cranfield University) Full-time

ENTRANCE QUALIFICATIONS: Honours degree. Grade: 2.2. **Other Selection Criteria:** Ability to speak French, interview. **STUDENT NUMBERS: Annual Applications:** 5 (1992). **Annual Places:** 2 (1992). **EMPLOYMENT ENTERED:** Energy and environmental management eg British Council, NIFES, British Gas, Grace (France), Hiross (Venice), Aerospatiale, European Patent Office. **COURSE PROFILE:** The course includes: chemical engineering (UTC, Compiegne); energy management; environmental auditing; fuel combustion; heat transfer; pollution; global warming; energy and environmental conservation; computer-aided control; economics.

CRANFIELD UNIVERSITY
Environmental Diagnostics
MSc 1 or 2 years Full- or Part-time

ENTRANCE QUALIFICATIONS: Undergraduate degree. Grade: 2.2 or above. **STUDENT NUMBERS: Annual Applications:** 100+ (1994). **Annual Places:** 24 (1994). **EMPLOYMENT ENTERED:** Materials and manufacturing industries, water companies, local councils and regulatory bodies, medical and public health, research and testing laboratories, consultancy. **COURSE PROFILE:** The course covers: biological processes; analytical methods; waste and waste water analysis; advanced analytical technology; environmental legislation; environmental management reports.

CRANFIELD UNIVERSITY
Energy and the Built Environment
MSc 1 year Full-time

ENTRANCE QUALIFICATIONS: Undergraduate degree. Grade: 2.2 or above. **STUDENT NUMBERS: Annual Applications:** 90+ (1994). **Annual Places:** 15 (1994). **EMPLOYMENT ENTERED:** Building services, civil engineering, consultancy, energy and environmental management. **COURSE PROFILE:** The course includes: energy and environmental overview; low energy design; life cycle costing; technical management; building services; heat transfer; solar energy processes; architecture and energy; energy monitoring and control.

CRANFIELD UNIVERSITY
Energy Conservation and the Environment
MSc 1 year Full- or Part-time

ENTRANCE QUALIFICATIONS: Undergraduate degree in engineering or applied science. Grade: 2.2 or above. **Other Selection Criteria:** Performance at interview. **STUDENT NUMBERS: Annual Applications:** 90 (1994). **Annual Places:** 20 (1994). **EMPLOYMENT ENTERED:** Energy and environmental consultancies, manufacturing and service industries, local and central government. **COURSE PROFILE:** The course covers: fuels and combustion; heat transfer; pollution and ecological protection; furnaces and boilers; thermal management; building services; combined heat and power; management for technology; energy and environmental law.

CRANFIELD UNIVERSITY
Water Pollution Control Technology
MSc 1 year Full- or Part-time

ENTRANCE QUALIFICATIONS: Honours degree in science or engineering. Grade: 2.2 or above. **Other Selection Criteria:** Interviews for likely candidates. **STUDENT NUMBERS: Annual Applications:** 450 (1992). **Annual Places:** 23 (1992). **EMPLOYMENT ENTERED:** Consultancies; plant contractors; equipment manufacturers; water companies. Firms offering placements include: Thames Water; Essex Water; Unilever; Welsh Water. **COURSE PROFILE:** The course provides training in process technology for water and wastewater treatment, from industrial and municipal waste waters through potable water to ultra-pure water. Group projects and an individual placement are included. This is a modular course.

CRANFIELD UNIVERSITY – SILSOE COLLEGE
Agroforestry
MSc 1 year Full-time

ENTRANCE QUALIFICATIONS: Degree, preferably in natural sciences, especially in agriculture, forestry or environmental science; engineering or humanities are acceptable. Grade: Good honours. **EMPLOYMENT ENTERED:** The course is intended for those wanting to work in agriculture or forestry development, with an emphasis on tropical locations.

CRANFIELD UNIVERSITY – SILSOE COLLEGE
Community Water Supply
MSc 12 months Full-time

ENTRANCE QUALIFICATIONS: Honours degree. Grade: 2.2 honours. **Other Selection Criteria:** Performance at interview. **STUDENT NUMBERS: Annual Places:** 10 (1992). **EMPLOYMENT ENTERED:** Work in water and sanitation projects world-wide, particularly in developing countries. **COURSE PROFILE:** The course includes: hydraulics; hydrology; water quality; water treatment; water engineering; microcomputer applications; groundwater development; rural water supply; water lifting and storage; health, sanitation and wastewater; irrigation and drainage; project; water well drilling.

CRANFIELD UNIVERSITY – SILSOE COLLEGE
Environmental Monitoring
MSc 1 year Full-time

ENTRANCE QUALIFICATIONS: Undergraduate degree. Grade: 2.2 or above. **Other Selection Criteria:** Performance at interview. **STUDENT NUMBERS: Annual Places:** 10 (1994). **EMPLOYMENT ENTERED:** Government, local government or quasi-government organisations (eg water authorities, advisory services, environmental protection agencies), government research laboratories and private consultancy firms. **COURSE PROFILE:** The course covers: data handling techniques; GIS; climatic systems and climatic change; water quality and testing; modelling environmental systems; applied remote sensing; aerial photographic interpretation; instrumentation; environmental project and policy management; ecological systems monitoring; water/air/land pollution monitoring; research project.

CRANFIELD UNIVERSITY – SILSOE COLLEGE
Environment and Landscape Engineering.
MSc 1 year Full-time

ENTRANCE QUALIFICATIONS: Undergraduate degree. Grade: 2.2. **Other Selection Criteria:** Performance at interview. **STUDENT NUMBERS: Annual Places:** 6 (1994). **EMPLOYMENT ENTERED:** Planning authorities, water authorities, mineral abstraction companies, amenity and leisure developers, estate agencies, conservation bodies. **COURSE PROFILE:** The course includes: land improvement engineering; grassland ecology and management; hydraulics; soil science and soil mechanics; soil and water engineering; habitat and amenity engineering; water management; hydrology and water resources; soil management; research project.

CRANFIELD UNIVERSITY – SILSOE COLLEGE
Environmental Water Management
MSc 12 months Full-time

ENTRANCE QUALIFICATIONS: Honours degree. Grade: 2.2 or above. **Other Selection Criteria:** Performance at interview. **STUDENT NUMBERS: Annual Places:** 20 (1994). **EMPLOYMENT ENTERED:** Consultant engineers; local and national authorities; conservation groups; agricultural consultants; farming organisations; landfill companies. **COURSE PROFILE:** The course covers: soil/plant/water relations; soil physics and water movement; hydrology and water resources; land improvement engineering; water quality and quality testing; environment engineering; ecology; economics; land drainage; soil erosion assessment and prevention; research project.

CRANFIELD UNIVERSITY – SILSOE COLLEGE
Irrigation Water Management
MSc 12 months Full-time

ENTRANCE QUALIFICATIONS: Honours degree. Grade: 2.2 honours. **Other Selection Criteria:** Performance at interview. **STUDENT NUMBERS: Annual Places:** 10 (1992). **EMPLOYMENT ENTERED:** Management of irrigation schemes world-wide, associated research, consultancy work. **COURSE PROFILE:** The course includes: soil/plant/water relationships; management; crop production; soil science; hydraulics; hydrology; microcomputer application; irrigation; agronomy; irrigation engineering; soil management and reclamation; field drainage; practicals; project.

CRANFIELD UNIVERSITY – SILSOE COLLEGE
Land Resource Management
MSc 12 months Full-time

ENTRANCE QUALIFICATIONS: Honours degree. Grade: 2.2 honours. **Other Selection Criteria:** Performance at interview. **STUDENT NUMBERS: Annual Places:** 25 (1994). **EMPLOYMENT ENTERED:** Government and private consultants engaged in overseas surveys for agricultural development; voluntary organisations; local authorities; environmental management and rural and countryside planning. **COURSE PROFILE:** The course covers: soil/plant/water relationships; management; GIS; economics; applied remote sensing; soil conservation; irrigation and drainage; resource survey methodology; hydrology; micro-computer applications; fieldwork; project; environmental classification and conservation.

CRANFIELD UNIVERSITY – SILSOE COLLEGE
Land Resource Planning
Diploma 9 months Full-time

ENTRANCE QUALIFICATIONS: Degree, BTEC HND or equivalent. **Other Selection Criteria:** Performance at interview. **STUDENT NUMBERS: Annual Places:** 15 (1992). **EMPLOYMENT ENTERED:** Voluntary aid organisations; government authorities/local authorities working in environmental management and rural and countryside planning; consultancy; surveys. **COURSE PROFILE:** The course includes: resource survey methodology; soil/plant/water relations; hydraulics; GIS; management; land resource planning; soil conservation; applied remote sensing; environmental classification; surveying; crop production; maths; integrated resource planning.

CRANFIELD UNIVERSITY – SILSOE COLLEGE
Range Management
MSc 12 months Full-time

ENTRANCE QUALIFICATIONS: Honours degree. Grade: 2.2 honours. **Other Selection Criteria:** Performance at interview. **STUDENT NUMBERS: Annual Places:** 10 (1992). **EMPLOYMENT ENTERED:** Extension workers; livestock and game managers; veterinarians working in the developing world. **COURSE PROFILE:** The course covers: hydrology; rural engineering; nutritional requirements of stock; ecological and social systems in range management; management; water supplies; remote sensing; soil conservation; economics of range management; project.

UNIVERSITY OF EAST LONDON
Environmental Science
MSc/Postgraduate Diploma 1 or 2 years Full- or Part-time

ENTRANCE QUALIFICATIONS: Undergraduate degree, or equivalent, in a biological or chemical discipline. Grade: 2.2 or above. **Other Selection Criteria:** Interviews for candidates who lack formal qualifications, but have experience in a relevant field and can provide evidence of being able to meet the demands of the course. **STUDENT NUMBERS: Annual Applications:** 25 Full-time and 25 Part-time (1994). **Annual Places:** 15 Full-time and 20 Part-time (1994). **COURSE PROFILE:** The course consists of taught elements, a syndicate exercise and a project. The major areas of biological monitoring, pollution monitoring and land reclamation/restoration are covered, to provide a thorough basis for the formulation of environmental audit, risk and impact assessments.

UNIVERSITY OF EDINBURGH
Environmental Chemistry
MSc/Diploma 12 months Full-time

ENTRANCE QUALIFICATIONS: Honours degree in chemistry, or other disciplines with appropriate chemical experience. **STUDENT NUMBERS: Annual Applications:** 40 (1994). **Annual Places:** 10 (1994). **EMPLOYMENT ENTERED:** Environmental consultancy, pollution control and monitoring, industrial research and environmental analysis. **COURSE PROFILE:** Six months instruction by internal and external staff via lectures, tutorials, placements, case studies etc and six months research into the key chemical aspects of the atmospheric, terrestrial and biotic environments, including ecological/health impacts and control/remediation measures. **FUTURE DEVELOPMENTS:** Optimally there will be sixteen places available in 1995/6.

UNIVERSITY OF ESSEX (Course taught in conjunction with Writtle College)
Crop Production in the Changing Environment.
MSc 1 Year Full- or Part-time

For details see Writtle College.

UNIVERSITY OF GLAMORGAN
Energy and Environmental Management
MSc 1 year Full-time 3 years Part-time

ENTRANCE QUALIFICATIONS: Honours degree or HND/C and experience. **Other Selection Criteria:** Interview. **STUDENT NUMBERS: Annual Applications:** 10 Full-time, 6 Part-time (1994). **Annual Places:** 7 Full-time, 5 Part-time (1994). **COURSE PROFILE:** The course is part of a suite of MSc awards centred around the three areas of health and safety, total quality and energy and the environment, reflecting the core activities in modern organisations.

UNIVERSITY OF GLAMORGAN
Environmental Conservation Management
MSc 1 or 2 years Full- or Part-time

ENTRANCE QUALIFICATIONS: Good honours degree in an environmental science subject. **Other Selection Criteria:** Interview, references. **STUDENT NUMBERS: Annual Applications:** 150+. **Annual Places:** 15 (1994). **EMPLOYMENT ENTERED:** Civil engineering and other areas. **COURSE PROFILE:** Course units include: Principles of Conservation

Management; Freshwater Conservation; Environmental Economics; Waste Disposal; Environmental Law; Coastal Conservation; Environmental Measurement (Analytical Chemistry); Agriculture and Conservation; Environmental Philosophy; Habitat Creation; Environmental Assessment; Conservation Modelling. A special feature of the course is the undertaking of a project in cooperation with an environmental agency.

UNIVERSITY OF GLAMORGAN
Quality and Environmental Management
MSc 1 or 3 years Full- or Part-time

ENTRANCE QUALIFICATIONS: Honours degree or HND/C and experience. **Other Selection Criteria:** Interview. **STUDENT NUMBERS: Annual Applications:** 7 Full-time, 6 Part-time (1994). **Annual Places:** 4 Full-time, 4 Part-time (1994). **COURSE PROFILE:** This course is part of a suite of MSc awards centred around the three areas of health and safety, total quality management and energy and the environment, reflecting the core activities in modern organisations.

GLASGOW CALEDONIAN UNIVERSITY
Energy and Environmental Systems
MSc/Postgraduate Diploma/Postgraduate Certificate 1 or 2 years Full- or Part-time

ENTRANCE QUALIFICATIONS: Undergraduate degree Grade: 2.1 or above preferred. **Other Selection Criteria:** Interview. **STUDENT NUMBERS: Annual Applications:** 100+. **Annual Places:** 30 (1994). **EMPLOYMENT ENTERED:** Environmental economics/consultancy, environmental impact assessment, energy management, NRA, ETSU. **COURSE PROFILE:** Energy, in production and use, is a pollutant. Thus this course deals with energy technologies, environmental sciences, and related socio-economic issues. It is designed for technologists, scientists and non-scientists alike. The modular structure is particularly suited to part-time students.

UNIVERSITY OF GREENWICH
Environmental Conservation
Postgraduate Diploma/MSc 2 years Part-time

ENTRANCE QUALIFICATIONS: Honours degree in one of the life or environmental sciences or a similar course which included a reasonable amount of ecology. Grade: 2.2 or above. **Other selection criteria:** Other qualifications or vocational experience considered. **EMPLOYMENT ENTERED:** The course is designed to produce professional practitioners with a broad range of skills. **COURSE PROFILE:** The course offers a selection of units and specialist subjects some of which are quite radical and challenging in their approach. It comprises a core of four compulsory units together with a project and a choice of optional units. The degree is part of the CATS Scheme and 120 credits must be taken to obtain the degree. A field course forms part of the core programme. **FUTURE DEVELOP-MENTS:** Intended to offer a one year full-time option in the near future. Applying for professional accreditation by the Institute of Ecology and Environmental Management and by the Institution of Environmental Sciences.

UNIVERSITY OF GREENWICH
Environmental Modelling
Postgraduate Diploma/MSc 2 years Full-time (Part-time available)

ENTRANCE QUALIFICATIONS: Honours degree in environmental sciences, mathematical and statistical sciences, physical sciences, earth science, life science, engineering. Grade: 2.2 or above. **Other selection criteria:** Entrance qualifications relaxed if candidate has considerable and relevant experience. **COURSE PROFILE:** An integrated and holistic approach to the mathematical and statistical modelling of the fate of pollutants and their impact on the environment. It includes units in: Atmospheric transport processes; processes in the aquatic environment; environmental geochemistry; mathematical and computational methods; statistical modelling methods; environmental chemistry; modelling methodology; environmental impact and management.

UNIVERSITY OF GREENWICH
Environmental Risk Assessment
Postgraduate Diploma/MSc 1 or 2 years Full- or Part-time

ENTRANCE QUALIFICATIONS: Honours degree in environmental science or environmental health. Grade: 2.2 or above. **Other selection criteria:** Other science graduates working for environmental consultancies or in environmental health or those in other related areas of work. **EMPLOY-MENT ENTERED:** The aim of the course is to produce graduates who are capable of making rational risk assessments and of modelling processes which involve hazards to human and other forms of biological life. **COURSE PROFILE:** The central focus of the course is environmental risk and risk assessment in the area of pollution control. The course focuses on advanced aspects of environmental chemistry, physics and toxicology areas which will provide students with the necessary background to appreciate aspects of fate measurement and prediction for chemicals released to the environment. The course endeavours to develop an appreciation of environmental modelling and the necessary skills to set up and manipulate simple models. The majority of the course units are assessed by essays, seminar presentations or some other form of continuous assessment.

GWENT COLLEGE OF HIGHER EDUCATION
Environmental Management
Postgraduate Diploma 1 or 2 years Part-time

ENTRANCE QUALIFICATIONS: Undergraduate degree or professional qualifications/experience. **Other Selection Criteria:** Interview. **STUDENT NUMBERS: Annual Applications:** 25 (1994). **Annual Places:** 20 (1994). **EMPLOYMENT ENTERED:** Most students are sponsored by a company or organisation and are therefore either already working as, or working towards becoming: environmental managers, project managers, chemists, planning officers, technical services etc. **COURSE PROFILE:** The course comprises six modules (Environmental Law; Waste Management, Eco-systems; Environmental Impact Assessment; Contingency Planning/Rick Assessment; Management Planning), each has built in assessment. Each module requires attendance for ten, three hour evening sessions. Completion of all six modules is required for the award.

HERIOT-WATT UNIVERSITY
Marine Resource Management
MSc/Postgraduate Diploma MSc 12 months Full-time Diploma 9 months Full-time

ENTRANCE QUALIFICATIONS: Undergraduate degree in: a science, engineering, geography, surveying or estate management. Grade: 2.2 or above, for MSc. **Other Selection Criteria:** Possible interview. **STUDENT NUMBERS: Annual Applications:** 80 (1994). **Annual Places:** 28 (1994). **EMPLOYMENT ENTERED:** Crown Estate Office (Marine Estate section), environmental consultancy (eg WS Atkins, Wimpy Environmental Ltd., Babtie Environmental Sciences, Counter Spill Research Inc. etc.), water authorities (eg Anglian Water), British Gas Exploration and Production, conservation bodies (eg Scottish National Heritage, South Downs Conservation Board) etc. **COURSE PROFILE:** This is an intensive modular course including: marine environmental processes; survey techniques; management of resources; resource valuation; development appraisal; and project management. A dissertation is also required for the MSc. The MSc course is RICS accredited and allows exemption from RICS professional examinations. Teaching sites are in Edinburgh and Orkney.

HERIOT-WATT UNIVERSITY
Marine Resource Development and Protection.
MSc/Postgraduate Diploma MSc 12 months Full-time Diploma 9 months Full-time

ENTRANCE QUALIFICATIONS: Undergraduate degree in a science, engineering or geography, or equivalent experience. Grade: 2.2 or above for the MSc. **Other Selection Criteria:** Interview possible. **STUDENT NUMBERS: Annual Applications:** 140 (1994). **Annual Places:** 37 (1994). **EMPLOYMENT ENTERED:** NRA, oil companies, fish-farm companies, environmental consultancy (eg Wallace Evans, Wimpey Environmental, Auris), government departments and agencies (eg SOAFD, Department of the Environment for Northern Ireland, Scottish National Heritage, English Nature, Crown Estate). **COURSE PROFILE:** There are two main options in this modular course, specialisation in Marine Environmental Matters (policy, monitoring, impact assessment, effluent treatment and control) or Bio-Resources (fisheries and aquaculture). A professional diving course is also available. Teaching sites in Edinburgh and Orkney.

UNIVERSITY OF HERTFORDSHIRE
Conservation and Recreation Management
MSc/Diploma 12 months Full-time

ENTRANCE QUALIFICATIONS: Undergraduate degree or equivalent experience. **Other Selection Criteria:** Academic references and interview. **STUDENT NUMBERS: Annual Places:** 10 Max. **EMPLOYMENT ENTERED:** Local authorities (planning and recreation departments), wildlife trusts, rural community councils, research consultants. **COURSE PROFILE:** Students choose from biological, conservation, recreation, management, rural planning, policies, agriculture, forestry, and fisheries units, as well as undertaking a project. Possibility of work experience.

UNIVERSITY OF HERTFORDSHIRE
Environmental Protection and Monitoring
MSc/Diploma 12 months Full-time flexible Part-time

ENTRANCE QUALIFICATIONS: Undergraduate degree or equivalent experience **Other Selection Criteria:** Academic references and interview. **STUDENT NUMBERS: Annual Places:** 10 Max. **EMPLOYMENT ENTERED:** Environmental consultants, local authorities, water companies, NRA. **COURSE PROFILE:** The course is centred around Environmental Monitoring plus a choice from: Industry and Environment; Biological Conservation; Geology of the Human Environment plus a project. Possibility of work experience.

UNIVERSITY OF HERTFORDSHIRE
Integrated Catchment Management
MSc/Diploma 12 months Full-time 2 years Part-time

ENTRANCE QUALIFICATIONS: Honours degree in biology, chemistry, civil engineering, environmental studies, geography, planning or other appropriate subject. **STUDENT NUMBERS: Annual Places:** 20 (1995). **EMPLOYMENT ENTERED:** New course, but it is anticipated that students will be employed in water companies and environmental consultants involved in catchment management. **COURSE PROFILE:** The course includes core modules in: Institutional and Legislative Frameworks; Natural Catchment Attributes; Systems and Techniques; Landuse and Catchment Planning. Options include: Catchment Hydrology and River Dynamics; Integrated Pollution Management; Hydropolitics and Environmental Economics; Management of Urban Drainage; Water Quality Management; Working Trends for Catchment Managers; plus and individual project (compulsory for the MSc).

UNIVERSITY OF HERTFORDSHIRE
(Offered by a consortium of ten institutions from 1995/96 with Council of Europe support)
European Environmental Management – Rural Areas
MSc 12 months Full-time

ENTRANCE QUALIFICATIONS: Undergraduate degree in a relevant subject, plus competence in a European language other than English. **STUDENT NUMBERS: Annual Places:** 20 (1995). **EMPLOYMENT ENTERED:** New course, students expected to undertake a wide range of environmental careers, throughout Europe. **COURSE PROFILE:** The first two taught units: Rural Areas in Contemporary Europe and Natural Resource Management are taught at the University of Hertfordshire. Sustainable Rural Development and Environmental Management Methodology and Structure are taught at the Rijkshogeschool IJselland, Deventer, Netherlands. A research project lasting 22 weeks is undertaken at any one of the ten participating institutions, which are located in eight countries in East, Central and Western Europe.

UNIVERSITY OF HULL
Environmental Analysis and Dynamics
MSc/Diploma MSc 12 months Diploma 8 months Full- or Part-time

ENTRANCE QUALIFICATIONS: Honours degree in an environment related subject and/or relevant work experience. Grade: 2.2 or above. **Other Selection Criteria:** Interview in some cases. **STUDENT NUMBERS: Annual**

SCHOOL OF GEOGRAPHY & EARTH RESOURCES

DEGREES IN ENVIRONMENTAL STUDIES

Co-ordinated interdisciplinary undergraduate and postgraduate degree programmes in environmental studies.

• **BSc in Environmental and Resource Management** provides an understanding of the management principles and problems associated with resource and environmental issues.

• **MSc/Diploma in Environmental Analysis and Dynamic** provides training in the monitoring, modelling and assessment of dynamic environmental systems.

• **MSc/Diploma in Environmental Policy and Management** provides training in the economic, political and legal dimensions of environmental policy and management. The course has been awarded an ESRC taught course studentship.

The School also offers supervision for higher degrees by research and studentships may be awarded by EPSRC, ESRC, NERC or BBSRC

For further information contact:
School Office, School of Geography & Earth Resources, The University of Hull, Hull HU6 7RX. Telephone 01482 465320/465385, Fax 01482 466340.

Promoting excellence in education & research.

 THE
UNIVERSITY
OF HULL

Applications: 80 (1994). **Annual Places:** 15 (1994). **EMPLOYMENT ENTERED:** Consultancies, research, local government and industry. **COURSE PROFILE:** The course provides experience in a range of scientific approaches presently employed in environmental assessment and analysis, as well as an understanding of environmental management and regulation. The emphasis is placed upon understanding the causes, effects and implications of environmental dynamism.

UNIVERSITY OF HULL
Environmental Policy and Management
MSc/Diploma 1 year Full-time up to 3 years Part-time

ENTRANCE QUALIFICATIONS: Undergraduate degree. Grade: 2.1 or above. **Other Selection Criteria:** Relevant professional qualifications and interviews. **STUDENT NUMBERS: Annual Applications:** 115 (1994). **Annual Places:** 25 (1994). **EMPLOYMENT ENTERED:** Consultancy, research, lecturing, local government. **COURSE PROFILE:** The course offers students the opportunity to build upon their existing knowledge and interests by providing (i) training in the economic, political, legal and sociological dimensions of environmental policy and management, and (ii) a critical approach to environmental policy analysis. The course offers a specialism in pollution regulation. **FUTURE DEVELOPMENTS:** Please contact the Postgraduate Secretary at the School of Geography and Earth Resources for up to date details.

UNIVERSITY OF HULL
Estuarine and Coastal Science Management
MSc/Postgraduate Diploma 1 year Full-time 2 years Part-time for MSc

ENTRANCE QUALIFICATIONS: Appropriate degree or experience, or HND and experience may be acceptable. Grade: Preferably a good honours degree. **Other Selection Criteria:** References and an informal interview where possible. **STUDENT NUMBERS: Annual Applications: 70** (1994). **Annual Places: 15** (1994). **EMPLOYMENT ENTERED:** NRA, RSPB, JNCC, consultancies, teaching (higher and further education), research (PhD, research assistants), waste management authorities, laboratory work etc. **COURSE PROFILE:** This is a multidisciplinary course covering the biology, chemistry, physical (sedimentology and oceanography), social, economic and legal aspects of estuaries and coasts. Overall there is a focus on human impacts and threats to these environments and the course concentrates on temperate areas. **FUTURE DEVELOPMENTS:** A new MSc 'Global Biodiversity: Conservation and Management' starts in 1995.

LANCASTER UNIVERSITY
Environmental and Ecological Science
MSc/Diploma MSc 12 months Full-time Diploma 9 months Full-time

ENTRANCE QUALIFICATIONS: Degree in a relevant science subject. Grade: 2.1 or above. **Other Selection Criteria:** Interviews. **STUDENT NUMBERS: Annual Applications: 200** (1994). **Annual Places: 28** (1994). **EMPLOYMENT ENTERED:** Research in universities, government institutions and industry, conservation (eg English Nature, RSPB), water authorities and NRA, local authorities, consultancy. **COURSE PROFILE:** The modular format allows for a highly flexible course structure. Particular emphasis is placed on the individual research dissertation. Strengths include: environmental pollution; water resource management; environmental impact assessment; vegetation survey; terrestrial ecology.

LONDON UNIVERSITY – BIRKBECK COLLEGE
Analytical Chemistry – Application to Conservation Science and Environmental Analysis
MSc 12 or 24 months Full- or Part-time

ENTRANCE QUALIFICATIONS: BSc in chemistry or a related subject.

Grade: 2.2, lower if applicant has considerable experience. **Other Selection Criteria:** Interview. **STUDENT NUMBERS: Annual Applications:** 16 (1992). **Annual Places:** 10 (1992). **EMPLOYMENT ENTERED:** Warren Spring Laboratory; Water Research Centre; Cory Environmental, Thurrock. **COURSE PROFILE:** The course provides a detailed study of the analytical techniques and methodology, with particular regard to environmental issues.

LONDON UNIVERSITY – BIRKBECK COLLEGE
Countryside Management
Diploma 2 years Part-time

Selection Criteria: Selection by application form. **STUDENT NUMBERS: Annual Applications:** 327 (1992). **Annual Places:** 25 (1992). **EMPLOYMENT ENTERED:** Wardens (eg National Trust, English Heritage), rangers (eg Countryside Commission), land managers, planners. **COURSE PROFILE:** The course provides the opportunity for students to acquire and develop the skills and knowledge necessary for the management of natural and cultural landscapes, including sites important to wildlife, archaeology, history and geology, that are often subject to intense and/or conflicting pressures.

UNIVERSITY OF LONDON – BIRKBECK COLLEGE
Environmental Science
MSc 2 years Part-time

ENTRANCE QUALIFICATIONS: Undergraduate degree in: botany; biological sciences; environmental science; geography or life sciences. **Other Selection Criteria:** Interview. **STUDENT NUMBERS: Annual Applications:** 70 (1994). **Annual Places:** 26 (1994). **EMPLOYMENT ENTERED:** Course is taken largely by those wishing to enhance existing careers. Current students include: school science teacher, lecturer, solicitor in environmental law, Thames Water employee.

UNIVERSITY OF LONDON – IMPERIAL COLLEGE
Environmental Analysis and Assessment
MSc/DIC (Diploma of Imperial College) 12 or 24 months Full- or Part-time

ENTRANCE QUALIFICATIONS: BSc in a suitable subject. Grade: 2.2 or above. **STUDENT NUMBERS: Annual Applications:** 92 (1994). **Annual Places:** 30 (1994). **EMPLOYMENT ENTERED:** Environmental consultancies, industry, regulatory authorities, postgraduate research. **COURSE PROFILE:** The first term centres around analytical techniques: chemical, physical and biological, using case studies and problem solving exercises.

The second term focuses on environmental assessment, including the mechanics of the surface environment and how the atmosphere, oceans and surface and ground waters interact. A major project is undertaken between April and September.

UNIVERSITY OF LONDON – IMPERIAL COLLEGE
Environmental Engineering
MSc 12 months Full-time

ENTRANCE QUALIFICATIONS: Undergraduate degree. Grade: 2.2 or above. **STUDENT NUMBERS: Annual Applications:** 120 (1994). **Annual Places:** 26 (1994). **EMPLOYMENT ENTERED:** Water industry, environmental and civil engineering, consultancy, government and regulatory authorities, research organisations. **COURSE PROFILE:** The course covers, control of pollution in the environment and the protection of public health through water supplies, wastewater treatment, air pollution control or solid waste disposal. The problems of both industrialised and less developed countries are discussed in detail.

UNIVERSITY OF LONDON – IMPERIAL COLLEGE
Environmental Technology
MSc/DIC (Diploma of Imperial College) 12 months Full-time

ENTRANCE QUALIFICATIONS: A good science or engineering honours degree. Grade: 2.2 or above. **Other Selection Criteria:** Work experience, references, interview. **STUDENT NUMBERS: Annual Applications:** 370 (1994). **Annual Places:** 70 (1994). **EMPLOYMENT ENTERED:** Students enter a wide range of environmental careers in industry, consultancies, research, government organisations and NGOs, eg Environmental Resources Ltd, Ove Arup Partnership, Coopers & Lybrand, IIED, Gibb Environmental Services, Greenpeace, NRA, National Power, English Nature, Conoco Ltd, UK CEED, MAFF, WS Atkins and CPRE. **COURSE PROFILE:** The course is divided into three parts. The compulsory Core Course in the first term covers: The Natural Environment; Environmental Perturbations; Environmental Management & Assessment; Environmental Policy; Environmental Law; Economics and Computing/Statistics. During the second term students specialise in one of the following options: Pollution; Energy Policy; Environmental Analysis and Assessment; Water Management; Ecological Management or Business & the Environment. The third term is devoted to an individual research project.

UNIVERSITY OF LONDON – IMPERIAL COLLEGE
Hydrology for Environmental Management
MSc 1 year Full-time

ENTRANCE QUALIFICATIONS: Undergraduate honours degree. Grade: 2.2 or above. **Other Selection Criteria:** Relevant experience. **STUDENT NUMBERS: Annual Applications:** 65 (1994). **Annual Places:** 18 (1994). **EMPLOYMENT ENTERED:** Civil and environmental engineering consultants, NRA, water companies, government research, university research and teaching. **COURSE PROFILE:** The course covers: hydrological processes; catchment hydrology; urban hydrology; irrigation; hydrogeology; groundwater flow and transport modelling; waste management and aquifer protection; water resource systems analysis; water resource management; water quality modelling and management; open channel flow; hydrometry; statistics; numerical modelling and computing.

UNIVERSITY OF LONDON – KING'S COLLEGE
Aquatic Resource Management
MSc 12 months Full-time

ENTRANCE QUALIFICATIONS: Undergraduate degree in biology, microbiology, environmental science, chemistry, ecology or geography. Grade: 2.2 or above. **Other Selection Criteria:** References and interview. **STUDENT NUMBERS: Annual Applications:** 128 (1994). **Annual Places:** 28 (1994). **EMPLOYMENT ENTERED:** UK water utilities, NRA England & Wales, Rivers Boards Scotland, environmental consultancies, research establishments, MAFF, industry, conservation bodies (eg Scottish National Heritage, English Nature) **COURSE PROFILE:** The course comprises a core module, Environmental Assessment and Analysis, and options drawn from: Ecotoxicology and Pollution; Inland and Estuarine Resource Management; Marine Resource Management; Fisheries Resource Management; Global Aspects of Water Management; Technologies for Developing Countries. An industrial placement forms and integral part of the content.

UNIVERSITY OF LONDON – ROYAL HOLLOWAY
Environmental Analysis and Assessment
MSc 1 year Full-time

ENTRANCE QUALIFICATIONS: Undergraduate honours degree in a science or science related subject. Grade: 2.2 or above. **Other Selection Criteria:** None. **STUDENT NUMBERS: Annual Applications:** 92 (1994). **Annual Places:** Up to 30. **EMPLOYMENT ENTERED:** First graduates 1994, so information not yet gathered. **COURSE PROFILE:** The course concentrates on the quantitative techniques by which the concentration of pollutant species can be accurately measured and applies these to the assessment of environmental impact and risk.

UNIVERSITY OF LONDON – UNIVERSITY COLLEGE LONDON
Conservation
MSc 12 months Full-time

ENTRANCE QUALIFICATIONS: Undergraduate degree. Grade: 2.2 or above. **Other Selection Criteria:** Interview, demonstrated commitment to conservation and relevant work experience. **STUDENT NUMBERS: Annual Applications:** 240 (1994). **Annual Places:** 20 (1994). **EMPLOYMENT ENTERED:** Governmental and non-governmental conservation agencies in the UK (English Nature, Countryside Commission, Wildlife Trusts), consultancies, European and international conservation agencies. **COURSE PROFILE:** The course begins with a two week introductory field course. This is followed by a series of modules, each dealing with a specific area of conservation in depth, assessed through group and individual project work. The modules are highly interactive, with considerable input from practising conservation specialists. **FUTURE DEVELOPMENTS:** Modular content may vary slightly from year to year.

UNIVERSITY OF LONDON – UNIVERSITY COLLEGE LONDON
Urban Development Planning
MSc 12 months Full-time

ENTRANCE QUALIFICATIONS: Undergraduate degree. **Other Selection Criteria:** Other relevant educational or professional experience may be considered in exceptional circumstances. **STUDENT NUMBERS: Annual Applications:** 85 (1994). **Annual Places:** 24 (1994). **EMPLOYMENT ENTERED:** Local government, academia, NGOs, national government in developing countries, international organisations (eg United Nations, ODA, Oxfam etc.). **COURSE PROFILE:** The course is designed to train participants in the linked processes of analysis, policy, planning, programming and management dealing with the issues of urban development, mainly in a developing country context. The course is concerned with a number of cross-cutting issues including environment, poverty and gender. Apart from policy and planning, it also offers a number of innovative specialisation areas, such as urban management and urban law.

UNIVERSITY OF LONDON – WYE COLLEGE
Applied Environmental Science
MSc 1 year Full-time

ENTRANCE QUALIFICATIONS: Honours degree in a biological, microbiological, chemical or biochemical science, or other equivalent qualifications. Grade: Minimum 2.2 honours. **Other Selection Criteria:** UK candidates normally interviewed, two academic references required, special consideration may be given to mature students with an appropriate background. **STUDENT NUMBERS: Annual Applications:** 25 (1994). **Annual Places:** 16 (1994). **EMPLOYMENT ENTERED:** PhD in soil microbiology; biotal, soil and groundwater remediation (Cardiff); LRZ Bio-energy Systems; Sydney Water Board. **COURSE PROFILE:** The course aims to impart a practical knowledge of environmental monitoring and to confer a scientific understanding of the modes of action of potentially harmful components within the biosphere. Also, by considering alternative environmental strategies and critical issues, and by the inclusion of courses on environmental law and economics, the scientific core of the course is placed in a framework of current concern. Following the taught course there is a three month research project.

LONDON SCHOOL OF ECONOMICS AND POLITICAL SCIENCE
Environmental Assessment and Evaluation
MSc 1 or 2 years Full- or Part-time

ENTRANCE QUALIFICATIONS: Honours degree in an appropriate discipline and/or appropriate professional experience. Grade: 2.1 or above. **STUDENT NUMBERS: Annual Applications:** New course. **Annual Places:** 10 (1995). **COURSE PROFILE:** The course covers: environmental planning; national and local level policy implementation; environmental impact; risk assessment; environmental data analysis; strategic environmental assessment; environmental auditing; cost-benefit analysis; environmental economics; sustainable development; decision making tools; and GIS. The programme includes: fieldwork, case studies presented by practitioners and a research project.

UNIVERSITY OF MANCHESTER
Applied Geology, Resources and Hazards
MSc/Diploma 12 months Full-time

ENTRANCE QUALIFICATIONS: Undergraduate degree in geology or a related subject. **Other Selection Criteria:** All students interviewed if possible. **STUDENT NUMBERS: Annual Applications:** c.20. **Annual Places:** 8 (1994). **EMPLOYMENT ENTERED:** Independent consultancy, ongoing research at University of Manchester. **COURSE PROFILE:** The taught component of this course consists of six modules: Raw Materials; Pollution

Control; Waste Disposal and Geologic Hazards; Energy Resources; Management and Communications Skills; and a special option. Selection of the special option and a research project gives the students the opportunity to tailor over half the course to meet individual training needs. **FUTURE DEVELOPMENTS:** The course is currently being restructured to fit the graduate school modularisation and there are plans to make the course available part-time.

UNIVERSITY OF MANCHESTER
Earth and Environmental Science Research Technologies
MSc 1 year Full-time 2-3 years Part-time

ENTRANCE QUALIFICATIONS: Degree in geology or related field/ physical science, from a recognised university. Grade: 2.2 or above. **Other Selection Criteria:** Good command of written and spoken English. Interviews to determine the particular requirements of applicants. **STUDENT NUMBERS: Annual Applications:** New course. **EMPLOYMENT ENTERED:** Potential employment areas include: environmental monitoring, environmental consultancy, research, science based industry and commerce. **COURSE PROFILE:** The course offers a compulsory core of taught modules on basic skills, followed by a flexible set of modules related to geoscience disciplines, specific research technologies and advanced knowledge. There is also a substantial individual research project chosen from a wide range of topics. **FUTURE DEVELOPMENTS:** Collaborative units with Geography, Biological Sciences and Engineering are planned, to make more optional modules available.

UNIVERSITY OF MANCHESTER
Pollution and Environmental Control
MSc 1 year Full-time

ENTRANCE QUALIFICATIONS: Degree in science or engineering. Grade: 2.2 or above. **Other Selection Criteria:** Interview, work experience. **STUDENT NUMBERS: Annual Applications:** 400 (1994). **Annual Places:** 55 (1994). **EMPLOYMENT ENTERED:** Water companies, NRA, waste management, Civil Service, environmental consultancies. **COURSE PROFILE:** The course consists of a taught component and a dissertation. The taught component contains three interrelated elements: (i) environmental law, economics and planning; (ii) treatment and control of pollutants of air, land and water; (iii) dispersion of pollutants into the environment and impacts on human health and the environment.

UMIST – UNIVERSITY OF MANCHESTER INSTITUTE OF SCIENCE AND TECHNOLOGY
Environmental Technology
MSc 1 year Full-time

ENTRANCE QUALIFICATIONS: Degree in engineering or applied physical science. Grade: 2.2 or above. **Other Selection Criteria:** Application requires support from two referees. **STUDENT NUMBERS: Annual Applications:** New course. **Annual Places:** 30 (1994). **EMPLOYMENT ENTERED:** It is anticipated that students will be employed in environmental consultancies, environmental regulatory agencies, process industries, water utility companies and general manufacturing industries and environmental management. **COURSE PROFILE:** The course covers: environmental legislation and enforcement policy; waste water engineering; air pollution mitigation; waste minimisation; process design for clean technology; waste management; pollution dispersion and monitoring; and risk analysis. A research dissertation is carried out between May and September for which a wide selection of topics are available.

UMIST – UNIVERSITY OF MANCHESTER INSTITUTE OF SCIENCE AND TECHNOLOGY
Integrated Pollution Management
MSc 2 years Part-time

ENTRANCE QUALIFICATIONS: Undergraduate degree in science or engineering, or an equivalent combination of educational and professional qualifications and experience. Grade: 2.2 or above. **Other Selection Criteria:** Application requires support from two referees. **STUDENT NUMBERS: Annual Places:** 25 (1994). **EMPLOYMENT ENTERED:** This course is designed as an 'in career training course' for persons wishing to develop the practical application of IPM. Course participants are usually in employment in industry, consultancy houses, and regulatory bodies including HMIP and the NRA. **COURSE PROFILE:** Participants attend ten, one week modules which cover all aspects of integrated pollution management, from the current legislative position to process design and waste minimisation. A research dissertation is undertaken in the latter part of the course, usually in line with the interests of the sponsoring employer.

MANCHESTER METROPOLITAN UNIVERSITY
Applied Environmental Science
MSc/Postgraduate Diploma/Postgraduate Certificate 1 year Full-time 3 years Part-time

ENTRANCE QUALIFICATIONS: Honours degree in science or relevant experience. **Other Selection Criteria:** Interview. **EMPLOYMENT ENTERED:** Environmental consultancies, senior management in relevant industries, research, pollution monitoring and control, nature conservation. **COURSE PROFILE:** The course covers the integration of appropriate applied sciences within the framework of monitoring and control.

MANCHESTER METROPOLITAN UNIVERSITY
Countryside Management
MSc/Postgraduate Diploma/Postgraduate Certificate 1 year Full-time 3 years Part-time

ENTRANCE QUALIFICATIONS: Appropriate undergraduate degree and/or experience. **Other Selection Criteria:** Interview. **STUDENT NUMBERS: Annual Applications:** 50 (1992). **Annual Places:** 30 (1992). **EMPLOYMENT ENTERED:** Most students are already employed in countryside management as wardens/rangers, or in local authority planning/ conservation offices etc. **COURSE PROFILE:** The course integrates ecological, physical and human aspects of countryside management and includes a large expert practitioner input.

MANCHESTER METROPOLITAN UNIVERSITY
Geographical Information Systems
MSc/Postgraduate Diploma MSc 3 years Part-time Diploma 18 months Part-time

ENTRANCE QUALIFICATIONS: Relevant undergraduate degrees, professional qualifications, experience. **Other Selection Criteria:** Application forms, telephone interviews, references. **STUDENT NUMBERS: Annual Places:** Approx. 45. **EMPLOYMENT ENTERED:** Most students taking this course are already in employment: utilities, local government, environmental organisations, education. **COURSE PROFILE:** This is a distance learning course undertaken in conjunction with the University of Huddersfield and the University of Salford. The course comprises twelve modules and three residential workshops, topics include: an overview of GIS; spatial thinking; attribute and spatial data; analysis, acquisition and quality of data; organisational issues; project design.

MIDDLESEX UNIVERSITY
Conservation Policy
MA/Postgraduate Diploma/Postgraduate Certificate 2 years Part-time

ENTRANCE QUALIFICATIONS: Undergraduate degree or equivalent professional experience (eg town planning, architecture, chartered survey-ing, working with an environmental agency). Grade: Good honours degree. **Other Selection Criteria:** Candidates are invited for interview. **STUDENT NUMBERS: Annual Applications:** 16 (1994). **Annual Places:** 15 (1994). **EMPLOYMENT ENTERED:** Employment with environmental agencies eg English Nature, Countryside Commission, Groundwork Trust, CPRE; higher education lecturing on conservation issues; local government en-vironmental/recycling officer. **COURSE PROFILE:** The course is aimed at those working in, or seeking employment in, environmental agencies, but is not overtly vocational. The overall aim is to explore what conservation policy means for society and deals with both built and non-built environ-mental issues in the UK.

NAPIER UNIVERSITY – EDINBURGH
Biology of Water Resource Management
MSc/Postgraduate Diploma 48 weeks Full-time

ENTRANCE QUALIFICATIONS: Honours degree in a biological subject or an honours degree in a science with appropriate biological content. **Other Selection Criteria:** The 'Entrance Qualifications' are the minimum entry requirement, applicants are selected according to the quality of their qualifications and experience. **STUDENT NUMBERS:** Annual Appli-cations: 80 (1994). Annual Places: 16 (1994). **EMPLOYMENT ENTERED:** Water industry; NRA; water PLCs; river purification boards; drainage and water supply authorities; fisheries laboratories; water research laboratories; industry (waste treatment, toxicity testing); and environmental consultants. **COURSE PROFILE:** The course provides education in the causes, effects and control of water pollution and in the management of water resources, including both marine and freshwater environments. The taught course (32 weeks) is organised into seventeen modules. The research project (16 weeks) is undertaken on a placement in the water industry.

UNIVERSITY OF NEWCASTLE UPON TYNE
Environmental and Resource Assessment
MSc/Diploma 1 year Full-time

ENTRANCE QUALIFICATIONS: Any relevant honours degree and/or appropriate professional qualification and/or experience. Grade: Good honours degree. **Other Selection Criteria:** Applicants considered on the basis of individual experience. **STUDENT NUMBERS: Annual Appli-cations:** 9 (1994). **Annual Places:** Up to 10. **EMPLOYMENT ENTERED:** New course. **COURSE PROFILE:** The course includes core modules in: Soil and Land Resource Assessment; Agrohydrological Resource Assessment; and Biological Resource Assessment, together with GIS/Remote Sensing, Quantitative Techniques and Environmental Economics. A wide range of optional modules, plus a major research project, allow the students to gear the course towards their individual interests.

UNIVERSITY OF NEWCASTLE UPON TYNE
Irrigation
MSc 12 months Full-time

ENTRANCE QUALIFICATIONS: BSc/BEng in a relevant area. Grade: 2.2 or above. **Other Selection Criteria:** Interviews. **STUDENT NUMBERS: Annual Applications:** 30 (1994). **Annual Places:** 12 (1994). **EMPLOYMENT ENTERED:** Irrigation equipment suppliers, consultancy, government agencies. **COURSE PROFILE:** The core course modules are: Soil and Land Resource Assessment; Agrohydrological Resource Assessment; Hydraulics; Soil-Plant-Water Relation; Irrigation Design; Irrigation Management; and Information Technology and Presentation Skills. Joint programme Civil Engineering and Soil and Water Engineering. The course also includes three months field studies in Malaysia.

UNIVERSITY OF NEWCASTLE UPON TYNE
Pest Management
MSc/Diploma MSc 1 year Full-time Diploma 9 months Full-time

ENTRANCE QUALIFICATIONS: Relevant honours degree or appropriate vocational qualifications for the MSc, and/or working experience for the Diploma. Grade: Good honours degree. **Other Selection Criteria:** Experience in a relevant job is accepted in place of high paper qualifications. **STUDENT NUMBERS: Annual Applications:** MSc 21, Diploma 5 (1994). **Annual Places:** MSc 8, Diploma 2 (1994). **EMPLOYMENT ENTERED:** Environmental agencies, universities and colleges, pest control companies, producers of pesticides (eg Shell), agricultural growers. Many students return to their employers in overseas countries. **COURSE PROFILE:** The course gives a thorough grounding in the theory and application of the biological principles for the practical control of animal pests, plant diseases and weeds affecting agricultural crops. It includes biological, chemical and integrated methods for the minimisation of environmental impacts. There is a strong emphasis on: entomology; applied ecology; invertebrate pathology and quantitative methodology.

UNIVERSITY OF NORTHUMBRIA AT NEWCASTLE
Environmental Monitoring and Control
MSc/Postgraduate Diploma/Postgraduate Certificate 12 or 36 months Full- or Part-time

ENTRANCE QUALIFICATIONS: Degree in a science or engineering subject. **STUDENT NUMBERS: Annual Applications:** 30 Full-time, 40 Part-time (1994). **Annual Places:** 6 Full-time, 32 Part-time (1994). **EMPLOYMENT ENTERED:** Employers of part-time students include: local authorities; water industry; chemical manufacturing; waste management; environmental consultants. **COURSE PROFILE:** The course is divided into three main parts. (i) One semester devoted to environmental monitoring, six taught units including chemical analysis, sampling and microbiology. (ii) One semester on environmental control covering: waste management; environmental law; built environment; air pollution management. (iii) A collaborative project involving an external company.

UNIVERSITY OF OXFORD
Environmental Change and Management
MSc 1 year Full-time

ENTRANCE QUALIFICATIONS: Undergraduate degree. Grade: 2.1 or above. **Other Selection Criteria:** Interview, relevant experience, commitment. **STUDENT NUMBERS: Annual Applications:** 85 (1994). **Annual Places:** 19 (1994). **EMPLOYMENT ENTERED:** Consultancy, NGOs, local authorities. **COURSE PROFILE:** This is a broadly based course covering: issues and driving forces; techniques and methodology; environmental science; managing the environment; plus in-depth study in two units. Students are required to complete a 15,000 word dissertation.

UNIVERSITY OF PORTSMOUTH
Environmental Engineering
MSc/Postgraduate Diploma MSc 12 months Full-time up to 5 years Part-time
Diploma 6 months Full-time

ENTRANCE QUALIFICATIONS: Honours degree in science, engineering or management related subject, or HND plus five years industrial experience. Grade: 2.2 or above. **Other Selection Criteria:** Interview required. Industrial experience is taken into account. **STUDENT NUMBERS: Annual Applications:** 100 (1994). **Annual Places:** 15–20. **EMPLOYMENT ENTERED:** Environmental managers/officers in companies, public corporations and consultancies. **COURSE PROFILE:** The modular MSc course

THE INTEGRATED GRADUATE DEVELOPMENT SCHEME (IGDS)

MSc IN ENVIRONMENTAL ENGINEERING

The IGDS in Environmental Engineering is a modular MSc Scheme presented in partnership with industry.

The Masters Degree provides an essential qualification for a career as an Environmental Manager, Auditor, Consultant or Project Manager, Engineer or Technologist with responsibility for environmental issues.

Delegates study a series of one week modular courses covering such subjects as Environmental Law, EU Directives and Integrated Pollution Control with specialist modules relating to the Water, Energy and Manufacturing industries. An Environmental Audit and a major project are carried out in industry.

The course may be studied full time or part time.

For further details, please contact:

**Dr G R Jordan,
Course Co-ordinator,
Integrated Graduate Development Scheme,
Anglesea Building, Anglesea Road,
Portsmouth PO1 3DJ
Tel: (01705) 842357
Fax: (01705) 842329**

A Centre of Excellence for University Teaching & Research

University of Portsmouth

consists of a series of week long courses, which are assessed by a post-modular assignment. It is a broad based course providing knowledge and understanding of environmental engineering, environmental and integrated pollution control, plus specialist modules relevant to the water, energy and manufacturing industries. 45% of presenters are currently practising in industry.

READING UNIVERSITY
Renewable Energy and the Environment
MSc/Postgraduate Diploma 12 months Full-time

ENTRANCE QUALIFICATIONS: Undergraduate degree in a science, engineering or technology subject. Grade: 2.2 or above for the MSc, any grade for the diploma. **Other Selection Criteria:** Some informal interviews. **STUDENT NUMBERS: Annual Applications:** 60 (1994). **Annual Places:** 10 (1994). **EMPLOYMENT ENTERED:** University research, consultancy, NGOs, government posts (overseas). **COURSE PROFILE:** The course covers the principles of renewable energy conversion and utilisation, with an awareness of the environmental impact of energy conversion. The main specialisms are: land; hydro; solar; biomass. There is an emphasis on project work and applications.

ST ANDREWS UNIVERSITY
Applied Environmental Geoscience
MSc/Diploma 1 year Full-time

ENTRANCE QUALIFICATIONS: BSc degree in geoscience (geology, geochemistry, geophysics, environmental geology). Grade: 2.2 or above. **Other Selection Criteria:** Interview. **STUDENT NUMBERS: Annual Applications:** New course. **Annual Places:** 12 (1995). **EMPLOYMENT ENTERED:** New course. **COURSE PROFILE:** The course consists of a core module in Environmental Impact Assessment, plus four option modules to be chosen from: Applied Sedimentology; Applied Geochemistry; Applied Geophysiscs; Applied Geomorphology; Minerals and Energy; Remote Sensing; Applied Hydrology; and Hydrogeology. Students also complete a compulsory research dissertation and research project.

UNIVERSITY COLLEGE SALFORD
Environmental Protection
MSc/Diploma for Advanced Studies 1 or 2 years Full- or Part-time

ENTRANCE QUALIFICATIONS: Honours degree in a relevant discipline for the MSc. Ordinary degree or HNC/HND with relevant experience for the Diploma. **Other Selection Criteria:** Interview. **STUDENT NUMBERS: Annual Applications:** 150 (1994). **Annual Places:** 20 Full-time, 15 Part-time (1994). **EMPLOYMENT ENTERED:** Local authority environmental health, chemical and glass industries, enforcement authorities (eg waste regulation authorities), environmental consultants. **COURSE PROFILE:** The course adopts a multidisciplinary approach to the solution of environmental pollution problems, and has a strong vocational character. Full-time students do a 12 week work placement. The course covers: environmental policy; law and resources management, together with research methods and air/water/land/noise pollution.

SCOTTISH AGRICULTURAL COLLEGE – ABERDEEN
Sustainable Agriculture
MSc 12 months Full-time

ENTRANCE QUALIFICATIONS: Undergraduate degree in a relevant subject. Grade: Honours. **STUDENT NUMBERS: Annual Applications:** 38 (1994). **Annual Places:** 12 (1994). **EMPLOYMENT ENTERED:** Field trials officer, research, farm management. **COURSE PROFILE:** The course explores the scientific basis of sustainable agriculture in temperate and tropical situations. Areas of study include: biological functioning; environmental impact; animal welfare; and economics and marketing. The course is run jointly with the University of Aberdeen and the Macaulay Land Use Research Institute.

UNIVERSITY OF SOUTHAMPTON
Integrated Environmental Studies
MSc 1 year Full- or Part-time

ENTRANCE QUALIFICATIONS: Undergraduate degree in a relevant science or engineering subject. Grade: 2.1 or above. **Other Selection Criteria:** Relevant experience will be considered. **STUDENT NUMBERS: Annual Applications:** 99 (1994). **Annual Places:** 13 (1994). **EMPLOYMENT ENTERED:** New course. **COURSE PROFILE:** This is a modular course with core units in Environmental Assessment, Environmental Economics and Environmental Law. Students register for a specialist theme in either Environmental Science, Education or Engineering, however there are a wide selection of options under any of these headings. **FUTURE DEVELOPMENTS:** The course will be reviewed at the end of the first completed session.

SOUTH BANK UNIVERSITY – LONDON
Environmental Monitoring and Assessment
MSc/Postgraduate Diploma 1 or 2 years Full- or Part-time

ENTRANCE QUALIFICATIONS: Honours degree in a science or science related subject. **Other Selection Criteria:** Other qualifications and/or a substantial period of relevant employment will be considered. **STUDENT NUMBERS: Annual Applications:** 40 (1994). **Annual Places:** 20 (1994). **COURSE PROFILE:** The course provides the skills to manage the collection and interpretation of environmental data. Study covers the methods of environmental monitoring, from the immediate environment to large scale ecosystem assessment.

UNIVERSITY OF STIRLING
Environmental Management
MSc/Diploma MSc 12 months Diploma 9 months Full- or Part-time

ENTRANCE QUALIFICATIONS: Undergraduate degree. Grade: 2.1 or above. **Other Selection Criteria:** References and previous experience. **STUDENT NUMBERS: Annual Applications:** 211 (1994). **Annual Places:** 36 Full-time, 4 Part-time (1994). **EMPLOYMENT ENTERED:** Environmental consultancy; river, forestry and waste management. **COURSE PROFILE:** The course is broken-down into three areas. (i) Core elements: Information

Technology; Environmental Assessment; Environmental Economics; Environmental Policy and Management; Environmental and Ecological Systems. (ii) Optional elements, students choose three units from twelve. Popular courses include: Environmental Project Appraisal; Coastal Zone Management; Pollution Control; River and Estuarine Management. (iii) MSc students complete a dissertation.

UNIVERSITY OF STRATHCLYDE
Environmental Studies
MEnvS/Diploma MEnvS 12 months Full-time Diploma 9 months Full-time
(Both can be extended to allow for part time study)

ENTRANCE QUALIFICATIONS: Honours degree in any discipline. **Other Selection Criteria:** Other qualifications and practical experience would be considered. **EMPLOYMENT ENTERED:** This broadly based course offers entry into a wide range of environmental careers in the public and private sector. **COURSE PROFILE:** A multidisciplinary course including study of modules in: Analysing and Understanding the Environment; Policy and Decision-Making for Environmental Change; Management and Environmental Action; Environmental Techniques. Masters students conduct a short research thesis on a practical environmental problem.

UNIVERSITY OF STRATHCLYDE
Environmental Studies for Environmental Managers in Business
MEnvS/Diploma MEnvS 12 months Full-time Diploma 9 months Full-time
(Both can be extended to allow for part time study)

ENTRANCE QUALIFICATIONS: Honours degree in any discipline. **Other Selection Criteria:** Other qualifications and practical experience would be considered. **EMPLOYMENT ENTERED:** Careers in environmental management in business organisations and consultancies. **COURSE PROFILE:** A multidisciplinary course including study of modules in: Environmental Business Strategy; Environmental Management Systems; Environmental Economics; Environmental Law; Relevant Environmental Assessment and Analysis. Masters students conduct a short research thesis on a practical business problem.

UNIVERSITY OF STRATHCLYDE
Environmental Studies for Officers in Conservation Organisations
MEnvS/Diploma MEnvS 12 months Full-time Diploma 9 months Full-time
(Both can be extended to allow for part time study)

ENTRANCE QUALIFICATIONS: Honours degree in any discipline. **Other Selection Criteria:** Other qualifications and practical experience would be considered. **EMPLOYMENT ENTERED:** Careers in national environmental agencies, central and local government and environmental pressure groups. **COURSE PROFILE:** A multidisciplinary course including the study of modules in: Environmental Conservation Policy Issues; Conservation Project Management; Relevant Environmental Assessment and Analysis. Masters students conduct a short research thesis on a practical conservation management project.

UNIVERSITY OF STRATHCLYDE
Environmental Studies for Safety Managers
MEnvS/Diploma MEnvS 12 months Full-time Diploma 9 months Full-time (Both can be extended to allow for part time study)

ENTRANCE QUALIFICATIONS: Honours degree in any discipline. **Other Selection Criteria:** Other qualifications and practical experience would be considered. **EMPLOYMENT ENTERED:** Careers in safety, health and environmental management. **COURSE PROFILE:** A multidisciplinary course including study of modules in: Health and Safety; Risk Assessment; Safety Management Auditing; Environmental Management Systems; Appropriate Environmental Assessment and Analysis. Masters students conduct a short research thesis on a practical safety management problem.

UNIVERSITY OF STRATHCLYDE
Environmental Studies for Environmental Professionals in Local Authorities and Public Sector Agencies
MEnvS/Diploma MEnvS 12 months Full-time Diploma 9 Months Full-time (Both can be extended for part time study)

ENTRANCE QUALIFICATIONS: Honours degree in any discipline. **Other Selection Criteria:** Other qualifications and practical experience would be considered. **EMPLOYMENT ENTERED:** A wide range of professional careers in local authorities and public sector agencies. **COURSE PROFILE:** A multidisciplinary course including study of modules in Environmental Policy Issues in Local Authorities and Public Sector Agencies, multidisciplinary Environmental Project Management and appropriate Environmental Assessment and Analysis. Masters students conduct a short research thesis on a practical local authority or public sector agency environmental management topic.

UNIVERSITY OF STRATHCLYDE
Environmental Science
MSc/Diploma MSc 12 months Full-time Diploma 9 months Full-time (Both can be extended for part time study)

ENTRANCE QUALIFICATIONS: Honours degree in a science discipline.

Other Selection Criteria: Other qualifications and practical experience would be considered. **EMPLOYMENT ENTERED:** A wide range of professional careers in public sector agencies, local and central government and private sector companies. **COURSE PROFILE:** The course covers the theoretical and practical knowledge of chemical, physical, biological and mathematical techniques for monitoring, modelling and managing the environment. Masters students complete a research or development project which forms the basis of a short thesis.

UNIVERSITY OF STRATHCLYDE
Public Health and Environmental Control Engineering
MSc/Diploma MSc 12 months Diploma 9 months Full- or Part-time

ENTRANCE QUALIFICATIONS: Honours degree (science or engineering) for the MSc, good HND plus experience for the Diploma. Grade: 2.2 or above for the MSc. **Other Selection Criteria:** Must be competent in basic calculus. **STUDENT NUMBERS: Annual Applications:** 45 (1994). **Annual Places:** 15 (1994). **EMPLOYMENT ENTERED:** Consulting engineers, local water authorities, NRA, river purification boards, industrial sector effluent control. **COURSE PROFILE:** The course offers specialist training in water and wastewater treatment and other fields of environmental control. Students gain a grounding in both the principles and the practises of water quality control and management. It is supported by excellent laboratory and computing facilities.

UNIVERSITY OF STRATHCLYDE
Water Engineering
MSc/Postgraduate Diploma MSc 12 or 21 months Diploma 9 months Full- or Part-time

ENTRANCE QUALIFICATIONS: Good degree in a relevant subject or HND with good experience. **Other Selection Criteria:** Must have mathematical ability. **STUDENT NUMBERS: Annual Applications:** 50 (1994). **Annual Places:** 15 (1994). **EMPLOYMENT ENTERED:** Consulting engineers, research organisations, water authorities, government departments. **COURSE PROFILE:** The course is intended for graduates who wish to gain further understanding of water supply, irrigation, flood studies, river engineering and water and wastewater treatment. It is supported by excellent laboratory and computing facilities and has been running for 35 years.

UNIVERSITY OF SUNDERLAND
Environmental Management
MSc 12 months Full-time 2-4 years Part-time

ENTRANCE QUALIFICATIONS: Honours degree. Grade: 2.2 or above. **Other Selection Criteria:** For any other degree, work experience and strong work references are required. **STUDENT NUMBERS: Annual Applications:** 82 (1994). **Annual Places:** 20 (1994). **EMPLOYMENT ENTERED:** Environmental consultancy, nature conservation, waste management, local authorities, environmental NGOs. **COURSE PROFILE:** The course has a broad ranging content including: land use; environmental assessment; pollution control; resource extraction; waste management; habitat conservation; countryside management; environmental auditing and management systems; environmental case studies and an industrial/work placement. The emphasis is on decision-making and management planning.

UNIVERSITY OF SUNDERLAND
UETP-EEE Environmental EuroPro
Diploma 2-5 years Part-time

ENTRANCE QUALIFICATIONS: Undergraduate degree or equivalent. **Other Selection Criteria:** Submission of an individually tailored study plan and programme. **STUDENT NUMBERS: Annual Places:** Individual programmes, so no set limit. **EMPLOYMENT ENTERED:** The course is designed for part-time students in current employment eg environmental management, land reclamation, environmental regulation, waste management, recycling, environmental auditing. **COURSE PROFILE:** Environmental EuroPro is a modern international system offering purpose built professional development for environmental management and engineering experts. Study plans are developed to fulfil the specific training requirements of individual professionals, utilising academic elements at the university and elsewhere, plus other training. **FUTURE DEVELOPMENTS:** The University of Sunderland is a UK centre for EuroPro, and will be able to assist in the development of study plans and registration of participants, whether on university programmes or not.

TRINITY COLLEGE CARMARTHEN
Environmental Protection
Diploma/MSc 2 years Part-time distance learning

ENTRANCE QUALIFICATIONS: Undergraduate degree and experience. **EMPLOYMENT ENTERED:** Students are seconded from industry and local authorities. **COURSE PROFILE:** This is a two-year distance learning provision, leading to a Royal Society of Health Diploma. It is concerned with air, land and water pollution and integrated pollution control.

UNIVERSITY OF ULSTER
Environmental Management
MSc/Postgraduate Diploma 1 year for the Diploma plus a further year for the MSc Part-time

ENTRANCE QUALIFICATIONS: Honours degree in an appropriate subject plus two years relevant experience or non-honours degree in an appropriate subject and five years relevant experience. **Other Selection Criteria:** Candidates without formal qualifications but with appropriate experience may be considered. **STUDENT NUMBERS: Annual Applications:** 20 (1994). **Annual Places:** 15 (1994). **EMPLOYMENT ENTERED:** Part-time course only, all students already employed. **COURSE PROFILE:** The course is designed for people already working in the environmental field who wish to develop a broader perspective on environmental management. The emphasis is on the achievement of practical and sustainable management solutions within both local and European contexts.

UNIVERSITY OF WALES – ABERYSTWYTH
Environmental Audit
MSc/Diploma 2 years minimum (up to 5 years allowed) Part-time by distance learning only

ENTRANCE QUALIFICATIONS: Undergraduate degree. Grade: 2.2 or above. **Other Selection Criteria:** Special consideration of non-graduates with appropriate experience. **STUDENT NUMBERS: Annual Applications:** 40 (1994) **Annual Places:** 19 (1994) **EMPLOYMENT ENTERED:** Many students are already in full-time employment, generally in consultancy. First graduates of the course will not complete until 1995. **COURSE PROFILE:** This is the first specialist course in environmental auditing, and is designed to equip graduates with the skills to undertake audits of company activities and to provide knowledge of the national and international legal and administrative framework of environmental audit.

UNIVERSITY OF WALES – ABERYSTWYTH
Environmental Impact Assessment
MSc/Diploma 1 year Full-time 2 years Part-time distance learning

ENTRANCE QUALIFICATIONS: Undergraduate degree. Grade: 2.2 or above. **Other Selection Criteria:** Special consideration of non-graduates with appropriate experience. **STUDENT NUMBERS: Annual Applications:** 150 full-time, 50 distance learning (1994). **Annual Places:** 35 full-time, 25 distance learning (1994). **EMPLOYMENT ENTERED:** Consultancies (eg ERM; RSK Environmental; Whelan; WS Atkins), public sector (eg NRA; Scottish National Heritage; English Nature; Countryside Council for Wales;

ADAS; local authorities), miscellaneous (eg Lloyds Register, CPRE, Institute of Environmental Assessment). **COURSE PROFILE:** The course aim is to provide students with a thorough understanding of EIA from the perspective of all participants in the process. Emphasis is on practical applications and on project management skills. The distance learning MSc includes residential schools.

UNIVERSITY OF WALES – BANGOR
Ecology – Theory and Techniques
MSc/Diploma 1 year Full-time
ENTRANCE QUALIFICATIONS: Degree in biological or related science. Grade: 2.2 or above. **Other Selection Criteria:** CV, references, interviews. **STUDENT NUMBERS: Annual Applications:** 115 (1994). **Annual Places:** 25 (1994). **COURSE PROFILE:** The course is designed to provide postgraduate students with a thorough grounding in modern ecological ideas and techniques; ecology being considered as a branch of natural science. The course is recognised by NERC and ESF. **FUTURE DEVELOPMENTS:** There are minor changes instituted every year.

UNIVERSITY OF WALES – BANGOR
Marine Environmental Protection
MSc/Diploma 1 Year Full-time
ENTRANCE QUALIFICATIONS: BSc (or by experience if over 30). Grade: 2.1 or above preferable. **Other Selection Criteria:** Usually interview. **STUDENT NUMBERS: Annual Applications:** 100 (1992). **Annual Places:** 15 (1992). **EMPLOYMENT ENTERED:** Aquatic consultancies, NRA, waterways board, environmental protection agencies, ICI, universities. **COURSE PROFILE:** The course covers: marine resource exploitation; environmental impact assessment; survey of temperate and tropical coastal habitats and communities; fisheries; biofouling; ecotoxicology; water quality and pollution analysis; coastal zone management and policy.

UNIVERSITY OF WALES – BANGOR
Rural Resource Management
MSc/Diploma 1 year Full-time
ENTRANCE QUALIFICATIONS: Undergraduate degree, HND, mature candidates with relevant experience considered on merit. Grade: 2.2 or above preferred. **Other Selection Criteria:** References and informal discussion if necessary. **STUDENT NUMBERS: Annual Applications:** 150 (1992). **Annual Places:** 40 (1992). **EMPLOYMENT ENTERED:** Countryside management, scientific officer, ranger, footpath officer, development projects with eg Countryside Council for Wales, English Nature, Forestry Commission, local authorities. **COURSE PROFILE:** The course aims to

present an integrated review of the scientific and socio-economic basis for management of rural resources. Three options are available (i) overseas rural development, (ii) conservation and (iii) soil resource management.

UNIVERSITY OF WALES – COLLEGE OF CARDIFF
Applied Environmental Geology
MSc 1 or 3 years Full- or Part-time

ENTRANCE QUALIFICATIONS: Undergraduate degree. Grade: 2.2 or above. **Other Selection Criteria:** Interview. **STUDENT NUMBERS: Annual Applications:** 60 (1994). **Annual Places:** 20 (1994). **EMPLOYMENT ENTERED:** Environmental geology and engineering geology (eg Wardell Armstrong, Theissens, Robinson Fletcher, structural soils, soil mechanics), hydrology (eg NRA) and landfill waste management (eg Llanelli Borough Council). **COURSE PROFILE:** Six month taught course, six month project. The taught course includes: hydrology; environmental pollution; applied geochemistry; land reclamation; soil and rock mechanics; engineering geology; environmental assessment and environmental law; computing and research skills. The project is undertaken with an industrial partner.

UNIVERSITY OF WALES – COLLEGE OF CARDIFF
Applied Hydrobiology
MSc 1 year Full-time

ENTRANCE QUALIFICATIONS: BSc **Other Selection Criteria:** Interviews required for NERC advanced course studentships. **STUDENT NUMBERS: Annual Applications:** 88 (1994). **Annual Places:** 20 (1994). **EMPLOYMENT ENTERED:** Over the last five years, two-thirds of graduates from this course have obtained employment with the NRA or water companies. **COURSE PROFILE:** The course covers: aquatic plants; computing biostatistics and modelling; fisheries biology and management; freshwater and estuarine biology; biology of polluted waters; toxicology; waste treatment; waste management; conservation. A research project is undertaken in collaboration with the water industry.

UNIVERSITY OF WALES – COLLEGE OF CARDIFF
Marine Resource Management
MSc/Diploma MSc 12 months Full-time Diploma 9 months Full-time

ENTRANCE QUALIFICATIONS: Undergraduate degree, or over 25 with suitable professional experience. Grade: Normally 2.2 or above. **Other Selection Criteria:** Interviews in certain case, considerable weight given to level of experience. **STUDENT NUMBERS: Annual Applications:** MSc 7, Dip. 3 (1994). **Annual Places:** MSc 2, Dip. 1 (1994). **EMPLOYMENT ENTERED:** Port authorities, conservancy boards, consultancy groups, river authorities, especially in the field of EIA. **COURSE PROFILE:** The course is concerned largely with the marine and coastal environment. There are three compulsory units, and students take up to three options, enabling them to tailor the course to suit their professional needs. A three month dissertation is part of the course. The course is combined with a transport option. **FUTURE DEVELOPMENTS:** The course will be modular as of 1995. This does not significantly affect the course content, only the methods of teaching and assessment.

WRITTLE COLLEGE (Course taught in conjunction with the University of Essex)
Crop Production in the Changing Environment
MSc 1 year Full-time

ENTRANCE QUALIFICATIONS: Honours degree in an appropriate subject or equivalent. Grade: 2.1 needed to obtain a scholarship, 2.2 otherwise. **Other Selection Criteria:** Interview. **STUDENT NUMBERS: Annual Applications:** approx. 50. **Annual Places:** approx. 15. **EMPLOYMENT ENTERED:** Agricultural research and consultancy, including: agrochemical industry (eg Rhone-Poulenc); plant breeders; government research institutes; commercial agriculture. **COURSE PROFILE:** The course covers: the principles of crop production and the physiology of crop yield; effects of stress on crop yield; analysis of current changes in the environment; pollution effects; water resources for agriculture; computer modelling of crop growth and production.

UNIVERSITY OF YORK
Environmental Economics & Environmental Management
MSc/Diploma MSc 12 months Full-time Diploma 9 months Full-time

ENTRANCE QUALIFICATIONS: Undergraduate degree in biology, economics or a related subject preferred. MSc students must have qualifications in both biology and economics, or complete the diploma as a foundation course. Grade: 2.1 or above for the MSc, flexible for the diploma. **Other Selection Criteria:** Interview for UK applicants. **STUDENT NUMBERS: Annual Applications:** 28 (1994). **Annual Places:** 5 diploma students in 1994, but numbers are flexible and reflect the number of good applications received. **EMPLOYMENT ENTERED:** MSc is new as of 1994/5, to date all diploma students have continued on the EEEM MSc, or another MSc course at the University of York. **COURSE PROFILE:** The programmes integrate teaching in biology, economics and EEEM itself. The diploma is a highly flexible course, tailored to students previous background. It can serve as a stand alone qualification or as a foundation year for the MSc.

REFERENCES

CAREERS

Useful publications

Careers in Conservation Royal Society for the Protection of Birds, The Lodge, Sandy, Beds SG19 2DL Tel: 01767 680551 An information pack.

Careers in the Environment The Environment Council, 21 Elizabeth Street, London SW1W 9RP Tel: 0171 824 8411
A leaflet covering the range of jobs available, training, work experience and further sources of information. Free but send A5 stamped-addressed envelope.

Careers in Environmental Conservation (Ed. McCormick & Donald) Kogan Page, 120 Pentonville Road, London N1 9JN Tel: 0171 278 0433, 5th edition (1992) ISBN 0749405236
Includes information on environmental jobs, work overseas, qualifications and experience, plus advice on finding job opportunities.

Courses and Careers in Sustainable Technology Centre for Alternative Technology, Machynlleth, Powys SY20 9AZ Tel: 01654 703743

Employment and Training Opportunities in the Countryside Countryside Commission Postal Sales, PO Box 124, Walgrave, Northampton NN6 9TL Tel: 01604 781848 Code no: CCP 256
A free leaflet on planning a career in countryside conservation and recreation.

Employment Opportunities with the Forestry Commission Forestry Commission, 231 Corstorphine Road, Edinburgh EH12 7AT Tel: 0131 334 0303
A 16 page leaflet on careers and jobs within the Forestry Commission; advises on minimum entry requirements.

Environmental Work – Institute of Biology Careers Leaflet Institute of Biology, 20–22 Queensberry Place, London SW7 2DZ Tel: 0171 581 8333
Describes jobs in environmental biology, and the qualifications and experience needed. Free on receipt of SAE.

Working in Agriculture and Horticulture Careers and Occupational Information Centre, PO Box 348, Bristol BS99 7FE Tel: 0117 9777199
A 24 page booklet outlining the various opportunities.

Working Out: Work and the Environment Council for Environmental Education, University of Reading, London Road, Reading RG1 5AQ Tel: 01734 756061 ISBN 0947613072
Gives information on choosing a career which will help the environment and shows how any job can be environmentally friendly. Includes case studies and information on ten different areas of employment.

Working with the National Trust National Trust, 36 Queen Anne's Gate, London SW1H 9AS Tel: 0171 222 9251
A leaflet explaining career and volunteer opportunities in all aspects of the Trust's work including horticulture, forestry, wardens and building staff. Free but send large SAE.

The Association of Graduate Careers Advisory Services (AGCAS) publishes various careers booklets. Further information from AGCAS, Central Services Unit, Crawford House, Precinct Centre, Manchester M13 9EP Tel: 0161 273 4233.

Careers, Education and Training for Agriculture and the Countryside (CETAC) produce a set of leaflets on career opportunities throughout the land based industries sector. They are free, but send large SAE to CETAC, c/o Warwickshire Careers Service, 10 Northgate Street, Warwick CV34 4SR Tel: 01926 412427.

The Countryside Management Association (CMA) produce a leaflet on the work of countryside rangers and wardens. Available from CMA, c/o Centre for Environmental Interpretation, Manchester Metropolitan University, St Augustines, Lower Chatham Street, Manchester M15 6BY Tel: 0161 247 1067. Please send a large SAE.

Finding a job

Environmental job advertisements can be found in the following newspapers and journals:

- All major newspapers, especially *The Guardian*, which has an environmental supplement on Fridays
- Local newspapers
- Environmental magazines such as *New Scientist*, *Nature*, *ENDS* (Environmental Data Services journal)
- Newsletters and magazines of environmental organisations.

The following recruitment agencies specialise in environmental employment:

CPL Scientific Employment Services, 43 Kingfisher Court, Newbury, Berks RG14 5SJ Tel: 01635 524064

Macmillan Davies, Salisbury House, Bluecoats, Hertford SG14 1PU Tel: 01992 552552.

EDUCATIONAL AND TRAINING COURSES

Useful publications

Action Breaks and Training Courses Scottish Conservation Projects, Ballallan House, 24 Allan Park, Stirling FK8 2QG Tel: 01786 479697. A free leaflet but please send a large SAE.

The Complete Degree Course Offers, Trotman & Co. Ltd, 12 Hill Rise, Richmond, Surrey TW10 6UA. Tel: 0181 332 2132.

Conservation Opportunities Conservation Volunteers Northern Ireland, 159 Ravenhill Road, Belfast BT6 0BP Tel: 01232 645169.
A free booklet on training courses, working holidays and weekend breaks. Please send a SAE.

Countryside Education and Training Directory (Order code CCP 363) and *Training for Countryside Managers, Staff and Volunteers* (Order code CCP 372)
Countryside Commission Postal Sales, PO Box 124, Walgrave, Northampton NN6 9TL Tel: 01604 781848
The Countryside Commission Education and Training Team also run a programme of sponsored training courses for those involved in countryside management. Courses are regionally organised. For English courses contact the Countryside Commission, John Dower House, Crescent Place, Cheltenham, Gloucestershire GL50 3RA Tel: 01242 521381; Welsh courses are run by Cyngor Cefn Gwlad Cymru, the Countryside Council for Wales, Plas Penhros, Ffordd Penrhos, Bangor, Gwynedd LL57 2LQ Tel: 01248 370444.

Developing Skills British Trust for Conservation Volunteers (BTCV) Training Department, Hollybush Farm, Broad Lane, Kirkstall, Leeds LS5 3BP Tel: 0113 2742335
BTCV provides over 500 residential and day courses around the regions for countryside staff and volunteers. Courses include practical conservation skills, task organisation and leadership.

Directory of Environmental Courses 1994–1996 The Environment Council, 21 Elizabeth Street, London SW1W 9RP Tel: 0171 824 8411
A guide to academic, professional and vocational courses related to the environment. It gives information on careers, continuing professional development, training and short courses as well as listing courses leading to recognised qualifications.

Degree Courses Guides Careers Research and Advisory Centre (CRAC). Biblios Publishers Distribution Service, Star Road, Partridge Green, West Sussex RH13 8LD Tel: 01403 710851

These guides cover individual subject areas and include information on course content, structure, and examination systems.

Entrance Guide to Higher Education in Scotland Committee of Scottish Higher Education Principals, St Andrew House, 141 West Nile Street, Glasgow G1 2RN Tel: 0141 353 1880
Gives information on courses and entry requirements for Scottish higher education. Updated annually.

Higher Education in the European Community: The Student Handbook Kogan Page, 120 Pentonville Road, London N1 9JN Tel: 0171 278 0433
Gives information on each European country's education system, institutions, qualifications, admissions procedures, language requirements and grants.

University and College Entrance: The Official Guide Sheed and Ward Ltd, 14 Coopers Row, London EC3N 2BH Tel: 0171 702 9899
A UCAS guide listing required grades for courses. Updated annually.

Further general sources of information on courses are publications by the Careers Research and Advisory Centre (CRAC). Further information from: CRAC, Sheraton House, Castle Park, Cambridge CB3 0AX Tel: 01223 460277.

Databases

Degree Course offers CD-ROM, Trotman & Co Ltd, 12 Hill Rise, Richmond, Surrey TW10 6UA. Tel: 0181 332 2132
Provides information on: A levels/careers and related degree courses; points required for courses at each institution; course highlights, and much more. Available in many schools and careers offices.
ECCTIS 2000 database ECCTIS 2000 Ltd, Fulton House, Jessop Avenue, Cheltenham GL50 3SH Tel: 01242 518724
ECCTIS 2000 is a database providing quick, easy access to information on nearly 100,000 award-bearing courses at universities and

colleges. It is available by subscription on a compact disc (CD-ROM) and can also be found in many secondary school, careers offices, adult guidance centres, libraries, Training Access Points, British Council offices and institutions of higher and further education.

PICKUP database PICKUP, Guildford Educational Services Ltd, 32 Castle Street, Guildford GU1 3UE Tel: 01483 579472.

PICKUP stands for Training, Industrial and Commercial Updating. The PICKUP Training Directory is available on a database which includes information on over 24,000 short, work-related training opportunities available in the UK. It contains courses from both the private and public sector and they range in length from half a day to three months. The Database on CD-ROM is available on subscription from ECCTIS 2000.

Training Access Points (TAP) are computer terminals giving access to databases such as ECCTIS and PICKUP. They can be found in some job centres and public libraries. For further information contact your nearest TAP or TEC office. (Information on location of TAP offices from The TAP Office, Sheffield College, Castle Centre, Granville Road, Sheffield S2 2RL Tel: 01742 731883.)

Institutions and professional bodies

Information on many more specialist and environmentally-related courses and careers may be obtained from professional bodies and institutions. Their addresses can be found in environmental directories such as *Who's Who in the Environment* and the *Directory of environmental courses* published by The Environment Council (see Directories section opposite).

Field study centres

There are over 1000 field study centres in Britain, many of which offer education and training courses. Further information from:

Field Studies Council (FSC), Central Services, Preston Montford, Montford Bridge, Shrewsbury SY4 1HW Tel: 01743 850674

The FSC is an independent educational charity which has 11 field centres in England and Wales. It offers a wide variety of courses on natural history, ecology and conservation, landscape, geology and many other topics. It also runs specialist overseas tours and teachers' courses.

National Association of Field Studies Officers (NAFSO), c/o Stouthall Environmental Education Centre, Reynoldston, Swansea SA3 1AP Tel: 01792 391086

NAFSO is the professional association for field study officers; it publishes a journal, newsletter and occasional papers.

Scottish Field Studies Association, Kindrogan Field Centre, Enochdhu, Blairgowrie, Perthshire PH10 7PG Tel: 01250 881286
Offers a range of courses on the environment, communications, community and management skills as well as core ranger training.

COSQUEC The Council for Occupational Standards and Qualifications in Environmental Conservation promotes training and education. Further information from COSQUEC, The Red House, Pillows Green, Staunton, Glos GL19 3NU Tel: 01452 840825

DIRECTORIES OF ORGANISATIONS

Many of the following directories can be found in public libraries.

Directory for the Environment
Green Print/Merlin Press, 10 Maldon Road, London NW5 3HR Tel: 0171 267 3399, 3rd edition, 1990 ISBN 1854250361

Directory of Environmental Consultants
Environmental Data Services Ltd, Finsbury Business Centre, 40 Bowling Green Lane, London EC1R 0NE Tel: 0171 278 4745

Directory of Environmental Courses 1994–1996 The Environment Council, 21 Elizabeth Street, London SW1W 9RP Tel: 0171 824 8411
A guide to academic, professional and vocational courses related to the environment. It gives information on careers, continuing professional development, training and short courses as well as listing courses leading to recognised qualifications.

Environment Business Directory
Environment Business, Information for Industry Ltd, 521 Old York Road, London SW18 1TG Tel: 0181 877 9130

Kelly's Business Directory
Reed Information Services, Windsor Court, East Grinstead, West Sussex RH19 1XA Tel: 01342 326972

Key British Enterprises (broken down by county)
Dunn and Bradstreet, Holmers Farm Way, High Wycombe, Bucks HP12 4UZ Tel: 01494 422000

Kompass: Register of British Industry and Commerce
Reed Information Services, Windsor Court, East Grinstead, West Sussex RH19 1XA Tel: 01342 326972

Who's Who in the Environment series
The Environment Council, 21 Elizabeth Street, London SW1W 9RP Tel: 0171 824 8411
England (1995) and *Wales* (1995) are available from The Environment Council. *Scotland* (1993) is available from Scottish Natural Heritage, Battleby, Redgorton, Perth PH1 3EW Tel: 0131 447 4784. *Northern Ireland* (1994) is available from Northern Ireland Environment Link (NIEL), 47a Botanic Avenue, Belfast BT17 1JL Tel: 01232 314944.